MYTHS AND LEGENDS OF ANCIENT EGYPT

The tales retold in this book are taken mostly from papyrus documents, and they represent probably only some of the aspects of ancient story-telling. What has survived can only be part of what was written down in antiquity; and what was written down must have been of special importance to have been written down at all. Some of the tales are religious, and they come from the extensive writings which constitute the body of Egyptian religious literature. Those given here demonstrate well the Egyptian's attitude to his gods—the way in which he endowed them with human feelings and the manner in which they vary in character from one cycle of legends to another. Many of the secular tales also have a religious basis and, like more modern oriental tales contain magic and mystery as important ingredients. Some stories, like *The Princess of Bakhtan,* represent a form of official propaganda in which tales based on historical events are used to justify acts of state. Whatever the purposes of the individual tales, however, they are all marked by strong narrative lines, and in all much use is made of direct speech. They reveal their origin as tales first made for telling.

A GROSSET ALL-COLOR GUIDE

MYTHS AND LEGENDS OF ANCIENT EGYPT

BY T.G.H. JAMES
Illustrated by Brian Melling

GROSSET & DUNLAP
A NATIONAL GENERAL COMPANY
Publishers • New York

CONTENTS

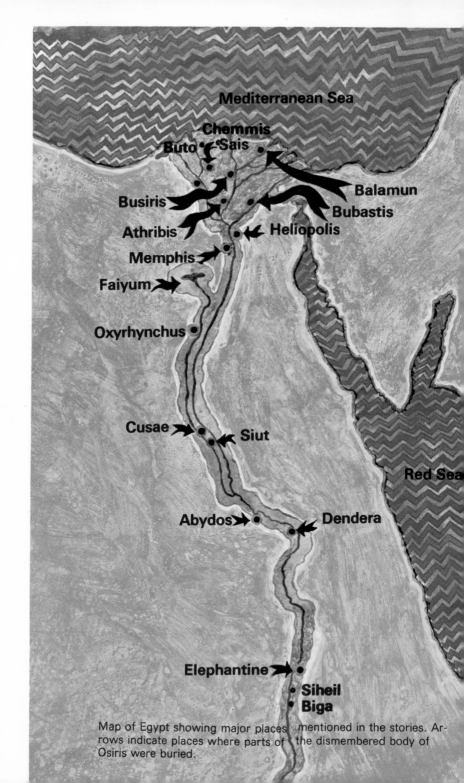

Mediterranean Sea

Chemmis
Buto • •Sais
Balamun
Busiris
Bubastis
Athribis
Heliopolis
Memphis
Faiyum

Oxyrhynchus •

Red Sea

Cusae • • Siut

Abydos • • Dendera

Elephantine •
• Siheil
• Biga

Map of Egypt showing major places mentioned in the stories. Arrows indicate places where parts of the dismembered body of Osiris were buried.

INTRODUCTION

It is merely one of the minor ironies of history that a survival of ancient Egyptian culture that has so fascinated people —the hieroglyphic writing—also signals how inaccessible the literature of the ancient Egyptians is to all but a few specialists. This need not be, since the Egyptians had a rich literature, one that developed alongside and expressed the changing patterns of their long and varied history. There was love poetry, for instance, and proverbs, biography and autobiography, folktales and legends, historical accounts of royal doings, and a whole body of writings that convey the realities of everyday life. And, of course, there was an extensive range of religious writings—prayers, prophecies, charms, hymns, myths, and much more.

We have gone into this rich treasure house of literature to assemble a display of only a few of its genres: specifically, those stories that we today distinguish as myths, legends, folktales, and historical fictions. The introduction to each story discusses its genre, or type, and sometimes it is relatively clear. That is, there will be a pure myth, telling about the gods, or a recognizable folktale, with a strong dose of magic and mystery. But we must be still clearer about something else: although we today may try to make such distinctions, the ancient Egyptians did not worry about drawing clear and firm lines between the natural and the supernatural, the real and the imaginary, this life and the afterlife, fiction and fact, men and gods. Even what is presented as history will see characters moving back and forth among these various worlds.

Now, we could present here a full 'lecture' on Egyptian literature, mythology, story-telling, and such matters. That would be one way to proceed—explicitly and straightforward and all at once. Instead, we have chosen to present the salient points in stages and as the issues are raised by particular stories. Thus, as our little anthology proceeds, we are also accumulating a sort of 'running analysis' of the background of Egyptian writings.

But there are a few basic and constant concepts that we

should be aware of from the outset. Chief among these is to be the prevalence of the gods and other religious elements in almost all the stories. Religion was a dominant factor in virtually every aspect of the life of ancient Egyptians. Food-production and the economy prospered because of the gods' concern; in turn, men set aside a certain part of their produce, profits, or labor for the gods. The kings were worshiped as supreme because they were considered the gods' representatives on earth; meanwhile, the king and his court were inextricably involved with the various priesthoods, their temples, and the many rituals. Scientific knowledge, the arts, architecture—including the construction of the magnificent pyramids and tombs—were all intertwined with religious beliefs. Practically all daily activities were permeated by men's desire to remain on the good side of the gods. We can understand little of the ancient Egyptians without an awareness of this pervasiveness of the gods and religious attitudes.

This is why, in part, it is so difficult to separate out the myths from the legends from the folktales from the historical fictions: the gods were everywhere. Of course, there were some more or less 'pure' myths—stories, for instance, that explained certain natural phenomena. And since, like most people, the Egyptians understood concepts better if they were presented through the medium of the personal and the specific, these myths involved a 'family' of gods.

Thus, although we do not give the story here, the ancient Egyptians had a creation myth—indeed, several creation myths, depending on the time and place of whoever was telling it. One that was widely accepted claimed that, in the beginning, the planet Earth was covered entirely with water. Out of this emerged a hill in the person of the creator-god, Atum. (In another, also familiar version, Amon-Re was the creator-god.) This Atum was all alone, but without a mate he gave birth to two children: the male, Shu, the air; and his sister, Tefnut, moisture. These two later had children of their own: another male, Geb, the earth; and his sister, Nut, the sky. Geb lay down across the surface of the water covering the Earth, and the seed of spring was first planted in his body. His parents, Shu and Tefnut, stood on Geb and raised their daughter, Nut, over their heads. Meanwhile, Geb and Nut, having fallen in love with each other, had produced four children: two girls, Isis and Nephthys; and two boys, Osiris and Seth. We shall encounter the subsequent doings of these gods in some of the stories to follow.

Recounting an Egyptian creation myth like that raises many questions, one of which we have referred to: it was by no means the only version of the creation that the ancient Egyptians subscribed to. And this raises another question that we shall encounter over and over again: the many contradictions in Egyptian myth and religion. This came about because there were so many strands—going back so far and drawing from so many different traditions—that got woven into the complicated pattern we today sum up as 'ancient Egyptian religion.' We must keep in mind that the ancient Egyptian culture that fostered these stories lasted some 3,000 years—a vast sweep of history, with all its changing generations and attitudes. Consider that the term 'Christian religion' has existed for only 2,000 years—and then think of all the different practices, beliefs, and so on that this embraces.

For one thing, each city or district had its own gods, starting far back in the dim past of pre-dynastic Egypt, in the most primitive soil of religion, with its totemic animals and vegetation-fertility gods. After the unification of the larger territories that were to make up Egypt (about 3100 B.C.), some deities came to be accepted by people of different regions, thus increasing the multiplicity of gods. Meanwhile, the Egyptians had gods for practically every branch of human activity and knowledge. Sometimes these gods were thought of as protecting specific trades and crafts or professions. There was Sakhmet, for instance, the wife of Ptah, a local god of Memphis; Sakhmet was the goddess of doctors. Or there was the ibis-headed Thoth, whom we shall meet frequently; he was the patron god of writing and calculation. And them there were the many household gods, such as Bes; he was a grotesque dwarf-demon who protected people against the many other demons. Ancient Egyptians seem hardly to have lifted a finger without invoking some god.

On another level, certain gods emerged in importance far transcending their local district origins. Such gods were usually promoted by different kings or priesthoods—and 'promoted' in the many senses of that word. Thus, Ptah of Memphis was credited by his own priests as being the creator of the world. And Amon was originally a tribal god of the region of Thebes, a city in Upper Egypt; by about 1600, Amon had merged with the sun god Re as Amon-Re and was worshiped as a supreme god throughout Egypt.

We shall be meeting some of these gods in the stories to come; there were so many hundreds of gods in ancient Egypt, and they took on so many varied forms and had so many varied attributes that we could not hope to encompass all of them. But for all we know about the gods of ancient Egypt, we must admit something else: we have very few complete and consecutive myths or stories about these gods. The existent religious texts—that is, those we know today —were composed for practical purposes—to be used in life for some ritual of worship, or in death for the well-being of the soul. What we have today, therefore, are a great body of prayers and other religious compositions with many incomplete and elusive references of the doings of the gods. From these we must piece together the myths and stories; from these, too, we may infer that the stories were well known to the ancient Egyptians.

Thus, what we read today is usually a composite 're-telling' of some ancient myth. And even with the other stories, it would be misleading to imagine that they all read smoothly in their extant originals. In some cases, there are only fragments or different versions; in other cases, there are missing sections, disputed phrases, and virtually un-translatable parts. We have usually given a 'smooth' reading that seems fairest and most sensible. Likewise, we have not bogged down in capturing the exact 'flavor' of each piece, although we have tried to convey the general tone.

For the originals of these many stories do vary considerably in style and tone. We might say that, as expected, the earlier ones, the myths, tend to be more archaic—more stilted, more naive, a bit cruder—than the later stories.

Here, however, we must be careful not to get confused by the fact that some of our versions of Egyptian stories are actually translations of Greek retellings of these stories. These Greeks have already taken the trouble of casting the Egyptian stories into their own more polished language and style. In passing, we might just note that much of what we know today about ancient Egypt has come to us filtered through the Greek language: thus, many of the names of kings and gods have been Hellenized—and the man we know as Cheops was really Khufu to the Egyptians.

Through all this, we must understand that what has survived is only a small part of what was written down in antiquity. And we may also assume that what did get written down must have been of some special importance to have been written down in the first place. In any case, myths and other stories were rarely written down in their full narrative form; they were handed down by word of mouth from generation to generation, whether in religious rituals or on story-telling occasions. The later tales, especially, are marked by a strong narrative line, and there is much use of direct speech—dialogue, in effect.

When these stories were first told, we can only guess in many instances—especially with the myths. When they first got written down is often hard to prove, although mention of historical figures (kings, princes, etc.) often provides a clue. But we cannot be sure whether the written document or inscription we possess today is but one of a long line of written accounts. For just as the Egyptians told and retold their stories over the centuries, they had them copied and recopied. This constant recopying also contributes to the number of versions differing in smaller or greater details.

The stories told in this book happen to be taken mostly from papyrus documents. Papyrus is a reed-like plant, whose fibers were processed and pressed to form a material on which the scribes could write with ink—thus providing the origins of both the process and the actual word for 'paper,' our own basic writing material. This papyrus would ordinarily be quite perishable, but it survived in Egypt mostly because of the extremely dry climate and the peculiarly 'dead' air of the tombs. The other major sources of our stories are the tomb paintings and inscriptions of stone monuments, and these, too, owe much to the Egpytian climate. But we shall be discussing the probable origins and the preserved sources of each of the stories in its own introduction.

But after all the introductions and explanations and backgrounds, there still remains something about this world you are about to enter into that cannot quite be explained. Let us admit, finally, that it is a foreign, strange, remote world at times, full of unknowns and unexpecteds. You must be prepared for many inconsistencies and oddities and 'missing links.' There are many marvelous happenings: just to name one, it is a world where male gods impregnate one another or bear young. All this requires you to extend your imagination, to suspend criticism, and, at times, simply to take things 'on faith.' In that way, you may truly enter into the world of the ancient Egyptians.

Along with the stories, you should enjoy glancing at the illustrations that capture the spirit of the ancient Egyptian world while illuminating it with a modern vision. There are also the pictures of actual archeological objects and structures that give a depth of reality to the context, and a map to 'place' events. Do not be afraid to check the list of major deities.

If you will let all these things fall into place, you can then relax and read these stories for their sheer pleasures. That, finally, is what the ancient Egyptians must have enjoyed in such stories.

PRINCIPAL EGYPTIAN DEITIES

Amon: a fertility god; became powerful and known as 'king' of the gods; linked with Re as Amon-Re; represented with ram-head.

Anubis: conductor of souls; god of embalming; represented as jackal.

Apis: the sacred bull.

Aten: the sun in the aspect of a solar disk.

Atum: a local sun god; promoted to creator-god; identified with Re; specifically the setting sun.

Banebdedet: a goat god.

Bast (or *Bastet*): lioness goddess; became cat goddess.

Bes: marriage god; protector against bad spirits; represented as hideous dwarf.

Geb: earth god; foundation of world; represented with goose-head.

Hathor: sky goddess; often represented as great cow; nurse of king of Egypt; also goddess of love, joy, dancing, music.

Hequet: frog-headed goddess; symbolized embryonic grain.

Horus: solar god; son of Isis and Osiris; took many forms but often represented with falcon-head.

Isis: sister-spouse of Osiris; potent sorceress; taught curing and domestic skills; cult widespread in later times.

Khnum: creation god; god of cataracts; represented with ram-head.

Khons: originally a moon-god; became wider known as healer.

Maat: goddess of Truth and Justice.

Meskhent: goddess of childbirth.

Neith: warrior goddess; became sky goddess, protectress of domestic arts; mother of Re.

Nephthys: daughter of Re; represented desert's edge.

Nun: god of watery abyss; represented waist-deep in water.

Nut: sky goddess; represented as starry body curved across sky.

Osiris: considered mythological king of Egypt who, after death, became lord of afterlife; possibly vegetation god.

Ptah: creation god; protector of artisans, artists.

Re: god of sun and creation; combined with Horus as *Re-Herakhty,* a solar god recognized throughout Egypt.

Sekhmet: goddess of war and battles; represented as lioness.

Seshat: star goddess; wife of Thoth; took on his associations.

Seth: god incarnate of evil, drought, dark, destruction.

Shu: god of air and supporter of the sky.

Tefnut: goddess of dew and rain; twin-sister of Shu.

Thoeris (or *Taueret*): hippopotamus goddess.

Thoth: moon god; spokesman of gods and keeper of records; patron of science, literature, wisdom, invention.

Elaborate pectoral decoration of gold and precious inlays from Tutankhamun's tomb. About 1300 B.C. Cairo Museum.

DESTRUCTION AND CREATION MYTHS

Among the many religious texts that decorate the walls of the tombs of Egypt's kings of the New Kingdom is one usually known as the Book of the Divine Cow. It consists mostly of an account of the last years of the rule of Re, the sun-god, on earth. The best surviving versions of the text occur in the tombs of Sethos I and Ramesses II (1318–1237 B.C.), two of the greatest of the kings of the 19th Dynasty. The earliest version, however, unfortunately incomplete, is found on the outermost of the great shrines that contained the coffins of Tutankhamon (c. 1352 B.C.). The texts are on the inside of the shrine and are illustrated by a scene in which the divine cow is shown in great size. Her belly, representing the sky, is decorated with stars, and just below it are two sun boats shown as if journeying across the heavens. The cow is supported in the middle by Shu, the god of the air, who keeps apart the sky and the earth; in his task he is helped by eight demigods of eternity. The myth that accompanies this scene is a strange tale of divine wrath, but it also includes an account of the creation of the heavenly bodies in a manner that persisted in Egyptian visual representation (if not in actual belief) until very late times.

The gilded wooden outermost shrine of Tutankhamon. About 1350 B.C. Cairo Museum

13

The Book of the Divine Cow

In the days before history began, the great god Re, who had created himself, ruled men as well as gods. He grew old, his bones were like silver, his flesh was like gold, while his hair was like real lapis-lazuli. Men began to plot against him, and word of the plot came to his ears. Re therefore sent for the gods of his entourage, including Nun the god of the Watery Abyss from which he had come. Re asked them to assemble in secret so that men would not know what they were about. When they had come and stood in order before the Majesty of Re, the gods begged him to tell them what was his trouble. Re then addressed Nun:

'O eldest one from whom I came, and you primeval gods! Men plot evil against me. What should I do? For I do not want to destroy them until I have heard your advice.'

'My son Re,' said Nun, 'who are greater than I from whom you came, and older than he who made you, sit quietly on

your throne. Great is the terror that reigns when your Eye,
the sun, proceeds against those who plot against you.'

'They have fled to the desert,' said Re, 'terrified that I
might speak to them.'

Together the divine company declared: 'Send out your
Eye to catch those who plot against you. No eye is better
for this task than yours. Let it go forth as Hathor.'

Acting on this advice, Re sent out his Eye in the form of
the goddess Hathor.

It was strange to find Hathor in a fearsome form, for she
was usually a gentle, benevolent goddess. But clearly she
was not always a kindly one; she was a goddess of terrible
anger, a suitable agent of terror who welcomed Re's order
with unexpected relish. She went in fury into the desert and
executed Re's vengeance on the men who had fled there.
When she came back after slaying great numbers of men, Re
welcomed her and congratulated her on her success. For this

deed, in later times, she was known as Sakhmet, a name that means Powerful One.

Unfortunately Hathor exulted in her bloody deed to such an extent that Re became worried that she might do more than he required. He was not a relentless god who desired the wholesale destruction of mankind, but one who wished only to teach men a lesson. So he sent for his swiftest messengers and ordered them to run to Elephantine to bring back a load of the bright red ocher found in that place.

When the messengers came back with the red ocher, Re ordered the High Priest of Memphis to come and pound the ore. Servant girls then set about brewing a vast quantity of beer, and the red ocher was mixed into it so that it looked like the blood of men.

Next day when dawn came and it was light enough for Hathor to start her slaying again, Re pronounced the beer to be excellent and ordered it to be carried to the place where she intended to perform her slaughter. 'I shall protect men from her,' Re said, and he ordered the drink to be poured out over the fields where Hathor would come. Seven thousand jugs were carried out by his attendants and emptied over the land, and the fields were covered all over.

After a little time Hathor appeared on the scene ready to renew her battle with men, thirsty for their blood. As she came over the land she found the fields flooded with the blood-red beer, and her face glowed marvelously with the light reflected from the liquid. Quite deluded by the trick, she thought it was indeed blood and she drank deeply, and it pleased her greatly. But soon the beer took its effect and she became drunk and wholly unable to recognize men and slaughter them.

When Hathor came out of her drunken torpor, her fury was gone, and she was welcomed back by Re as his Eye. Re ordained that from that time forward it should become customary for intoxicating drinks to be prepared for the goddess on all the feasts of the year; the preparation of the drinks was in the hands of servant girls.

Unhappily Re was not satisfied by the outcome of this episode, and he found to his regret that he still nursed a grudge against men. His fellow-gods tried to reassure him by reminding him of his omnipotence, but he was not con-

vinced, and complained to Nun, the Watery Abyss. 'My body is as weak as it was in the earliest times; I do not think I shall truly be powerful until the cycle of my existence comes round again.' Nun bid his daughter Nut, the sky goddess, assume the form of a cow and bear Re upon her back.

When men on earth saw this happen they were amazed, and some of them declared their intention of taking vengeance on their fellows who had caused Re to withdraw from earth. Darkness covered the earth when Re had gone; but as soon as light came again, those men took their bows and shot arrows against the enemies of Re. As soon as that god observed what was happening, he declared that slaughter had begun on earth; and it continued from that time onward.

Meanwhile in his lofty place set on Nut, Re began to create the heavenly bodies and the divine places, and he established himself in a vantage point from which he could observe men. All went well at first until Nut was overcome with dizziness at the height. So Re brought into being special deities whose job it was to support Nut, the heaven. Shu, the god of air, was also ordered to place himself beneath Nut to protect the divine supports. And Geb was instructed to look after the earth.

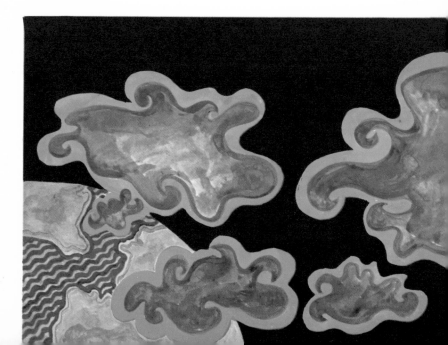

All was not yet settled, however, because Re in leaving men had deprived them of the light of his Eye, the sun. A substitute had to be provided, and he sent for the god Thoth and explained to him: 'Look here! I have now settled myself in heaven and my task is to provide light in the netherworld. I want you to act as my assistant on earth, to supervise all who are there. You will have to deal with any trouble that occurs, and in particular you must act as my deputy.' For these purposes Thoth's form as an ibis was brought into being, and as an ibis-headed god he served as the divine secretary and adjutant. But Re also required him to provide light, and so the moon of Thoth was created. For this purpose Thoth's form as a baboon was brought into being. Re declared, 'You shall be my representative, and when men see you they will be able to see through the darkness and will give praise for you.'

In this way the moon was created and Re compensated for his desertion of earth. So also was explained night and day and the creation of the firmament. In the eyes of the ancient Egyptians the sky was Nut whose body arched over the world whether she was shown as a cow or as a woman. Re was the sun by day, and when he disappeared at night his place was taken by the moon which was Thoth.

HUMAN PASSIONS IN THE GODS

Egyptian gods are shown in many texts to be the embodiments of specific human characteristics. The nature of Egyptian religion, however, is so complex that many of the best-known deities appear in different guises at different periods. (Re is sometimes benevolent, sometimes cruel; Hathor is usually kindly, but occasionally bloodthirsty, as in the last story.) There are many reasons for these variations in the presentation of divine characters, but not the least important is the human tendency to equip the gods with variable passions that reflect the fickle behavior of men. The primitive passion of jealousy, coupled with that of ambition, was commonly shown to be the dominant factor in the quarrels of the gods. It will be met shortly in the stories concerned with the struggles of Horus and Seth. It is the motive force also in a story in which Isis, usually the sweet mother-goddess and faithful wife, appears darkly plotting against Re, the lord of the universe.

The story is preserved in two papyrus documents, one in the Turin Museum and one in the British Museum. They date from the 19th Dynasty—sometime between 1320–1200 B.C., a period of considerable social and political ferment. As is so often the case with Egyptian texts, the two copies are not quite identical; but when we consider the conditions of the times in which they were produced, it is surprising how close they are. The great religious texts that are found repeated many times in temples and tombs were undoubtedly copied from standard versions; the copies therefore are usually very close to each other in precise wording. Copies of texts on papyrus, on the other hand, are frequently at variance with one another. Many of the differences are due to the fact that they were written down in some cases from oral dictation. The scribes clearly did not always catch what was being dictated and probably preferred to write nonsense than ask for a repeat. Happily the variants in the two versions of the present story are more helpful than confusing.

The goddess Isis with her divine symbol of a throne on her head.

Isis Challenges Re

Now Re was the great lord who created everything, heaven and earth, men and gods, all kinds of creatures. He was the king of men and gods and was infinitely varied in his forms and infinitely variable in his purposes. He was endowed with many names, some of which were so secret that they were unknown even to gods. The goddess Isis, however, became jealous of Re's omnipotence. As a result she began to think how she might usurp the power of Re and become the mistress of heaven and earth in his place. In her boundless desire to gain her end, she considered many ways by which she could defeat the great god; a physical victory would not be good enough. She had to achieve a mental ascendancy beneath which Re would be quite helpless. After much thought it occurred to her that one way by which she might succeed was by discovering the secret name of Re; to know the secret name would be to secure a hold over his power.

Every day Re came riding into the heavens in his divine boat, attended by a company of minor deities and spirits, and he established himself on the two thrones of the horizons. By this time, however, he had grown very old and was somewhat senile in his behavior, so that he tended to drivel. As he went along, his saliva fell on the ground, and Isis, coming behind him, took up some of this saliva mixed with the earth on which it had fallen. She worked these materials into a clay and from it fashioned a serpent in the form of an arrow. While it lay in her hand it remained without life, and in this form she put it down at the crossroads where Re would pass in his daily journey through the land.

When the great god, attended by his retinue, next went out on his course and arrived at the crossroads, the serpent came to life. Inspired by the magic placed on it by Isis, it sank its fangs into Re, and he let out a mighty howl that echoed throughout the heavens. 'What is that?' asked the company of gods. But the great god himself could not answer because an extraordinary weakness came upon him. His jaws chattered and his limbs shook as the poison from the serpent took possession of his body. He sank to the ground in terror, jerking as the spasms of pain ran through his body.

He was a miserable sight, no longer the great god, master of all creation.

For a time Re was completely helpless and could do nothing to indicate what was wrong; but it was not long before he was able to summon up enough strength to cry to those who were with him: 'Come here to me, all you who were created from my limbs, all you who came forth from me, and I'll tell you what has happened to me.' When they had gathered together and he had their attention, Re continued: 'I have been wounded by something quite deadly. I know in my heart that this is so, although my eyes never saw what it was, and my hand surely did not make it. I am certain that none of you would have done such a terrible thing to me. But I can tell you this: I have never felt pain like this pain. I am sure that there is no more severe pain possible.'

In his shocked condition Re set about reminding the gods just who he was, repeating to them his divine origins and pedigree. He also pointed out that his father had devised his name and that he was a god of many names. 'My father and my mother uttered my name, and it was concealed in my body so that no one could ever have the ability to cast a spell

over me. I came forth from my shrine, as I always do, and I began making my journey through the land I had created. Suddenly somebody or something struck at me, and I cannot guess what it was. My heart burns and my body shakes. Please, call together my children, especially those gods who know magic, who are clever at speaking, and whose knowledge can pierce even the heavens.'

The message went out, and the gods, the children of Re, began to gather. They came from all quarters of the universe in a state of great uncertainty, for few knew exactly what had happened. The rumors among them were wild, but all understood that something terrible had happened to Re. Was he truly on his death bed? They came prepared to lament over their father, but among them was Isis, and she came equipped with her magic, her mouth capable of administering the breath of life. With her spells and formulas she could drive out evils and revivify the dead. She spoke to Re: 'What is the matter, father? Has a serpent injected you with poison? Has a creature which you yourself created, lifted its head against you? There's no doubt that it can be destroyed by the right kind of helpful incantation. I can dispel it, if you so wish.'

In answer, Re explained how he had gone out to view the lands he had created and how he was bitten by something which he did not see. 'The effect is strange,' he continued. 'It is not like fire or water, and yet I am colder than water and hotter than fire. My body runs with sweat and yet I shiver. My eyes are glazed and I cannot see the heaven. My face is bathed in perspiration as if it were the height of summer.'

'Tell me your name,' said Isis.

'I am the creator of heaven and earth,' answered Re. 'I have joined the mountains and created the waters. I am the great procreator. I made heaven, and I established the horizons of East and West and set the gods in glory in them. When my eyes are open, it is light, and when they shut, it is dark. When I give the order, the Nile flood rises. My name the gods do not know. I have invented time and established

the festivals of the year. I created the fire of life by which all works are done. At the dawn I am Khepri; at midday, Re; and at evening, Atum.' This declaration did nothing to help, and the poison continued to run through his body.

'All that sounds well,' said Isis, 'but you have not actually told me your name. Tell me it, and I shall remove the poison from your body. He who states his name shall live.' As there seemed no abatement in the fury of the pain, Re then surrendered himself to Isis. 'I shall lend an ear to my daughter Isis, so that my name may pass from my body into her body. It was concealed within me by the most divine god, that I might sit easily in my boat in the heavens. Once it has passed out from my heart to you, you can tell it to your son Horus, but only after you have warned him solemnly against telling anyone else.' When he had made this statement he told his name to Isis, the great magician.

As soon as she had secured the name, Isis set about uttering a suitable spell to release Re's body from the poison that crippled it. And the poison passed from Re's limbs and he was wholly relieved.

OSIRIS—MARTYRDOM AND MYTH

Of all the Egyptian gods, Osiris is today one of the most familiar, just as he was one of the most popular among the ancient Egyptians. He possessed many divine functions, and in Egyptian religious texts he is assigned many different roles. But it is as the king of the dead that he is best known. From quite an early period, kings were identified with Osiris when they died. In later times, all Egyptians who felt qualified to memorialize themselves, considered that they too achieved this identification with the god when they died. So at death a man became Osiris, but he also entered into the kingdom of Osiris where he was judged and ruled by Osiris. Apparent contradictions of this kind were not uncommon in Egyptian religion; as we have observed in the introduction, such contradictions often grew out of the long history that lay behind a god before he entered the written records. Thus, Osiris originally was probably a god of vegetation; like all vegetation, he died away periodically; and like the vegetation that mattered most to the Egyptians, he was revived by inundation. Osiris' death and rebirth not only told the story of the Nile during its autumn recession and spring flood; the story also gave each man some hope for immortality. The common man, in particular, found many recognizable human elements in the story of Osiris and thus found that the cult of Osiris had a more personal meaning than, say, the cult of the sun god, who could seem remote and unattainable.

Despite his popularity, the many references to stories of Osiris are maddeningly incomplete and elusive. He is most commonly regarded as a king—a dead king—but no Egyptian text tells the whole story of his origin and fate. Yet there clearly existed a tradition of royal martyrdom according to which a king, possibly a historical figure, sacrificed himself, or was sacrificed, for the good of his people. The only continuous account is one preserved in a writing by the Greek author Plutarch, who lived in the first century A.D. Although it is so late in date, this account reproduces many of the details that occur in Egyptian texts of much earlier periods. There can be no doubt that the story, as told by Plutarch, is one version of the Osiris legend, as the ancient Egyptians knew it. It seems quite fair, then, to give Plutarch's version here, while indicating some of the major variations from other sources.

28

Osiris in the Tomb of Sennedjem, Thebes. He holds the crook and flail, signs of divine regal authority. About 1250 B.C.

The Life and Death of Osiris

The great god Re, it seems, learned that Nut and Geb had secretly loved one another; in revenge, Re laid a curse on Nut that she could give birth on no day of the year. Thoth, however, who was also in love with Nut, by trickery managed to secure enough parts of days to construct five extra days that could be added to the calendar of the year after its last day. These five days became the birthdays of the children of Nut, and the Egyptians named them as such. On the first was born Osiris; on the second, Horus; on the third, Seth; on the fourth, Isis; and on the fifth, Nephthys. Of these five gods, Nephthys and Seth married each other; so, too, did Isis and Osiris. It was said that the latter pair had fallen in love when they were still in the womb.

In time, Osiris became the king of the Egyptians, ruling them with benevolence. He rescued them from their rough and

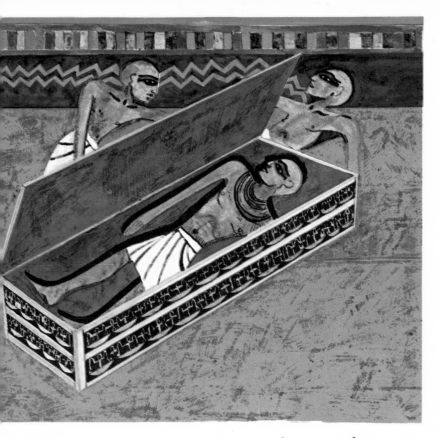

primitive way of life; he taught them argiculture, gave them laws, and instructed them in the worship of the gods. Afterward Osiris turned his attention to the rest of the world, bringing civilization to every place to which he went, winning the people over by sweet words and soft persuasion.

Seth was desperately jealous of his brother Osiris and decided to do away with him. While Osiris was away from Egypt, there was little Seth could do because Isis kept careful guard over her husband's interests.

As soon as he returned, however, Seth invited Osiris to a great banquet along with a large number of his own associates. Seth had, in advance, obtained the measurements of Osiris' body, and he engaged skilled cabinet-makers to construct a marvelous chest of just that size, finely decorated all over. In the course of the entertainment, the chest was brought into the great hall where they feasted, and Seth offered to present it to the guest who fitted it. One by one all his fellow conspirators came forward and tried the chest for size; in some cases it was too big, and in other cases, too small. Finally it was the turn of Osiris. When he stepped into the chest and lay down, it was seen to be a perfect fit. Immediately Seth and his followers closed in, slammed down the lid, closed the bolts, and sealed the chest with molten lead. Eager not only to kill Osiris, but also to dispose of his body, Seth instructed his followers to bear the coffin down to the river that flowed past his house and to cast it into the flood. With luck, the river would carry the coffin down to the sea and it and its contents would never again be seen.

In due course, Isis heard what had happened, and she set out in great sorrow to look for the chest. To mark her mourning, she cut off a lock of her hair and she dressed herself in special mourning garments. As Isis traveled about, she stopped everybody she met, asking if the chest had been seen. She even asked children, for they spend the time running about the countryside, seeing everything and noticing all the strange things that happen. In the end, it was some children who were able to tell Isis which of the mouths of the Nile had been used by Seth and his confederates.

What had happened to the chest after it had been thrown into the Nile was this. First it was carried down to the sea, and the current took it to the coast of the Lebanon, by the city of Byblos. Here the chest was cast up on the beach by the waves, and it came to rest in the branches of a sapling. As the tree grew it enfolded the chest within its trunk, and when it was fully grown the chest was quite invisible. The king of Byblos noticed this fine tree one day as he passed by; he had the upper, arched part, which enclosed the chest, cut down and made into a fine pillar to support the hall of his palace. In shape and size it was just right for this purpose, and his carpenters had only to trim off its side branches to make it fit perfectly.

Meanwhile, Isis in her search had heard a rumor that the chest had reached Byblos, and she also learned what had happened to it. So she came to Byblos and one day was found sitting by a well in a state of great distress. She would speak to nobody who approached her except the servants of the queen of Byblos. With these she made herself friendly, offering to

help them in their toilet. She did up their hair most deftly, breathing on them a fragrance that emanated from her whole being. Her skill in work of this kind was beyond the powers of mortals, and the maidservants were transformed in beauty of appearance. Moreover they carried everywhere the fragrance of the goddess, and all who smelled it were astonished by its allure. When the queen saw what had happened to her servants, she longed to see this unusual stranger who gave out such a wonderful fragrance, and she sent for her to come to the palace. At once the queen and Isis struck up a great friendship and the goddess was installed in the royal household as nurse to the queen's child.

At night, however, when it was time to nurse the child, Isis gave it her finger to suck instead of her breast; she also sought to make the child immortal by burning away the mortal parts of its body. At the same time, Isis turned herself into a swallow and flew around and around the pillar that enclosed the chest, lamenting loudly. The queen, who had secretly come to watch what went on, gave a great shriek when she saw her child on fire, and in so doing she broke the spell and prevented the child from becoming immortal. Isis then revealed herself to the queen and demanded the pillar so that she could retrieve the body of her husband. She took down the pillar without difficulty, cutting away the outer wood to reveal the chest within. The discarded parts of the tree she covered with linen and fragrant oil and gave them to the king and queen who had them placed in the temple of Isis in the city where they were honored as great relics.

With the chest carefully guarded, Isis took ship from Byblos and sailed back to Egypt. As soon as she reached land, at a place that was quiet and desolate, she took the chest from the boat, opened it and embraced the body of Osiris, weeping bitterly over his lifeless limbs. At this point, Isis' vigilance relaxed somewhat. The versions of the story found in Plutarch's narrative and in more ancient texts differ in many details, and it is not clear which is the most authentic and ancient. According to Plutarch, Horus was already born to Isis, and it was while she was going to see him that the subsequent tragedy occurred. The birth of Horus, however, in some versions comes later. What does seem clear is that for a time Isis left the chest in the marshes, and during the night Seth, out hunting, came upon it and recognized the body of his old enemy, Osiris. Knowing the magical skill of Isis, Seth determined to cheat her. He took the body, cut it up into many pieces, perhaps fourteen, perhaps sixteen, and scattered them throughout Egypt (see map, p. 4). He hoped that Isis would not be able to find them all; yet he knew that she would spare no pains in seeking them and in reassembling the body of her dead husband.

When Isis discovered what had happened, she set out again to search for her husband, this time assisted by her sister Nephthys. The search took them throughout the whole of Egypt from the Delta to Nubia, and slowly they found where each part lay. Some texts suggest that at each finding-place they held a funeral ceremony and buried the part. In this way many burial places of Osiris were established in the land. Of these, the most important for centuries was Abydos, and to Abydos all men came in death (in fact or by wish) on a sacred pilgrimage to be united with Osiris in death. In the latest period of Pharaonic Egypt, Abydos lost its importance to Biga, an island in the Nile at the First Cataract, which was also con-

sidered to be one of the burial places of the parts of Osiris'
body. The stories found in other texts, however, maintain
that as Isis and Nephthys collected the parts, they put together the body until it was whole, making the first mummy.
Again, Plutarch differs slightly, claiming that Osiris' penis
had been swallowed by an oxyrhynchus fish. By magic, Isis
was able to provide a substitute, but she was unable to fully
revivify the corpse. Yet so successful was she in her efforts
that she was able to conceive a child by him. Horus was
born, and he inherited Osiris' regal power on earth while
Osiris, forever the dead king, ruled the realm of the dead.
Thereafter, in death all men hoped to become Osiris.

MAGICAL ELEMENTS IN RELIGIOUS BELIEFS

Magic represented an important element in ancient Egyptian religion. It was also an ever-present factor in daily life; it was used not only to obtain specific ends when normal methods seemed inadequate, but also provide protection against dangers seen and unseen. Life in Egypt was usually made out to be idyllic, and life in the realm of the dead was always shown as a kind of reflection of earthly life. Yet there were hazards to be met on earth, and terrors that were difficult to combat without divine aid. The amulets that the Egyptians wore were simple protective instruments. More specific protection could be provided by written texts that were composed explicitly for prophylactic purposes. Snakes and scorpions were everyday hazards in Egypt, and magic might help to keep them away. But magic alone was not considered wholly reliable, and the Egyptian rarely put his trust entirely in the efficacy of uncertain powers. Magic could only help a perfectly reasonable method of action to be just a little more efficient.

A servant spinning flax thread on a spindle. From the Tomb of Khnumhotpe at Beni Hasan. About 1900 B.C.

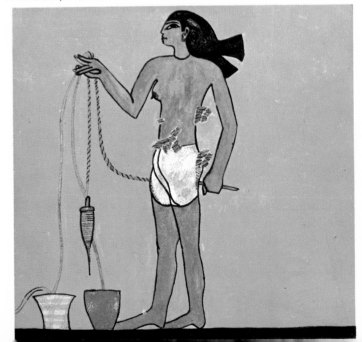

Among the greatest Egyptian gods, Isis was renowned for her magical powers; she was called 'the great one of magical spells'. She was credited with particular success in dealing with snakes and scorpions, and many inscriptions have survived from the later periods of ancient Egypt containing texts designed to protect specified persons from the bites and stings of these creatures. The texts mostly take the form of spells that need to be recited, and they incorporate myths from the ancient legends of the gods in which magic is used to dispel evil. The story told here consists of two parts, in both of which Isis employs magic to drive out poison. They belong to the cycle of legends concerned with Osiris and his martyrdom; these legends are set in the time after the death of that god while his son Horus was still a child. Beyond that, the two parts have been pieced together from various sources—papyri, inscriptions, etc.—for, as previously stressed, there exists no single text from ancient Egypt that recounts the complete sequence of events as described here.

The Wanderings of Isis and the Agony of Horus

When Isis was left at the mercy of Seth after the death of her husband, she was forced by Seth to enter a spinning house where she was kept working for him. Although Seth pretended that he kept her there for her own good, his intentions were far from honorable. He understood that his position and power in the future depended on whether he could prevent her son Horus from growing to manhood and claiming the throne of his father Osiris. Seth allowed Isis little freedom, and at first she felt herself incapable of escaping, for she was much hampered by her baby.

The position was intolerable, however, and she did not need much encouragement from Thoth to escape. He urged her to leave the spinning house, taking Horus with her: 'When he is grown up and his strength developed,' said Thoth, 'you can place him on his father's throne, and the rule over the Two Lands of Egypt may be given to him.' So when evening next came, Isis left the spinning house with Horus, accompanied by seven scorpions who were to cover her retreat. 'Take care not to give any clues of my path

to the evil one who will follow me,' she instructed them, 'until we get as far as the marshes of the Delta.'

When they came near a town and the place where women lived, a noble lady saw the little procession on the road and shut the door in Isis' face, for she was terrified at the sight of the scorpions. This cowardly behavior annoyed the scorpions, who arranged a suitable revenge. They all deposited their reserves of poison on the sting of one of their number, Tefenet.

Meanwhile, a fishergirl had taken pity on Isis and invited her into her humble house. No sooner had Isis gone in than Tefenet slipped into the house of the noble lady and stung her son. At the same moment the house burst into flames and there was no water handy to put out the fire; yet it rained, although it was the wrong season of the year. The lady was distraught because she did not know whether her son would live or die. She rushed about the town lamenting loudly, and Isis, when she heard the cries, took pity on her and her son who had done no wrong. 'Come to me,' she said, 'and I shall cure him. My father has taught me the secret of how to drive out poison.'

The lady brought the child to Isis, who placed her hands on him and uttered powerful spells to drive out the evil. 'Come out, poison of Tefenet,' she intoned, 'go to the ground. I am Isis, the mistress of magical spells. Every snake obeys me. Let the child live and the poison die.' And in her spell she identified the child with her own son Horus: 'Let Horus be well for his mother Isis, and let any creature who has been similarly struck down be well for his mother also.' Thus the poison left the child.

So grateful was the lady at the recovery of her son that she brought all her property and placed it in the house of the fishergirl. She realized that the evil had overtaken her because she had shut the door of her house on Isis and she brought the property as a recompense. In this way Horus became well for his mother Isis, and so too did anyone else become well who had been poisoned, and for whom the spells of Isis were recited.

Fishermen at work in the marshes. From the Tomb of Ipuy at Thebes. About 1250 B.C.

In the next part of this story, Isis is found with Horus in the marshes by the town of Chemmis in the Delta. Much of this part of Egypt was rough and uncultivated in ancient times. Here were wide stretches sparsely populated by man, ideal country for fugitives. Living in such surroundings was hard, but Isis had her compensation. She was thrilled to have Horus with her, because in him she saw the avenger of her husband, and for that reason hid him closely so that he might not be found by Seth. They were very much on the run, and Isis found it so difficult to support them both that she was forced to go out into the surrounding country begging for food. She took the form of a poor woman, and as she went from place to place she thought constantly of Horus. One day when she returned to their hiding-place, she was shocked to find her child lying apparently lifeless where she had left him. His eyes poured tears and his mouth was wet with spittle; his body was

relaxed and there was scarcely a trace of a heartbeat.

Isis' lamentation was bitter. She cried to the child, but he was too weak to answer. Her breasts were full, but he could not suck, though he was ravenous. The well was brimming, yet the child was thirsty. 'Who can help me?' she cried. 'My father is in the underworld, my elder brother is in his coffin, while my other brother is our enemy. What man can I call on?' In desperation she then shouted to the people of the marshes, for they alone were at hand. Fishermen came from their houses and hurried to help her, calling out, 'What a terrible thing has happened!' They did their best to drive out the evil that possessed Horus, but none of them had the right skills to effect a cure.

After some time a woman came who had a great reputation in her own town. She carried with her a sign of life, a most powerful amulet, and she was obviously wholly convinced of her skill. 'Don't be afraid, Horus', she said. 'Do not be downcast, mother of the god. The child is safe against the evil of his brother. Seth cannot come into this neighborhood, or go about in Chemmis. It is not he who has hurt him. The child has been poisoned by a scorpion or a snake.'

At once Isis checked this diagnosis; she smelled the breath
of Horus and tested him for other symptoms. When she found
that he had indeed been poisoned, she took him in her arms and
danced about like a fish on a griddle, renewing her lamentation:
'Horus has been bitten! Horus has been bitten! The young
one of Chemmis, the beautiful, sinless, fatherless, child has
been bitten! The son of the god whom I have tended, in
whom I saw the avenger of his father, has been bitten! Horus
has been bitten! Horus has been bitten!'

As she cried out, Horus began to weep, and the people
who stood around were much distressed. Her sister Nephthys
rushed up to see what all the fuss was about, and the scorpion
goddess Selkis came, asking 'What on earth is the matter with
the child? Sister Isis, call to heaven and the boat of Re will
come to a halt until things are well with Horus again.'

So Isis called to heaven and the divine boat stopped in its progress. Immediately Thoth was sent down to find out what the trouble was. He came fully equipped with magic, shouting out to Isis, 'What is the matter, Isis? I trust nothing has happened to Horus. For his protection is the boat of Re, and it has come to a halt today, and darkness reigns. Light will not come again until Horus recovers.'

'Indeed, Thoth,' said Isis, 'you seem very confident of your ability, but what exactly are your plans? Horus is struck down with poison, and there can be little doubt that Seth is responsible and that the death of Horus is intended. I wish I had not lived to see this moment, for ever since I conceived him I have longed to establish him as if he were his father.'

'Do not fear, Isis; do not cry, Nephthys,' answered Thoth. 'I have indeed come here with the breath of life to cure the child. Horus, may your heart be strong! Your protection is he who is in the sun-disk, who rules in heaven, who lights up the Two Lands. He is your protection in his many forms. Awake, Horus, for your protection is everlasting. Out, poison! The great god Re drives you away. His boat stands still and will not move until the patient is recovered. The wells are dry, the crops wither, and food is taken from men, until Horus is restored to health for his mother, Isis. Horus! Your spirit is your protection, and your attendants protect you. The poison is dead and its force is dispelled.' In this way did Thoth pronounce his magic, and at once Horus was restored to health. To all who stood around, Thoth proclaimed, 'Go home, for Horus lives for his mother.'

With an eye to future trouble, Isis then begged Thoth to instruct the inhabitants of Chemmis and the nurses of nearby Buto to assume responsibility for the care of the divine child whenever she was away; for little in Isis' circumstances had changed and she still had to go begging from place to place. This Thoth did, enjoining them, 'Watch over this child and divert his enemies until the day comes when he can assume the throne. Now I must go, to put the sacred boat into motion again and to report to Re that Horus is well and the poison powerless.'

A small stone pillar, dedicated to Horus and inscribed with magic charms. About 200 B.C. British Museum.

GODS IN ALL-TOO-HUMAN SITUATIONS

In Egyptian mythology one of the most persistent themes is that of the rivalry between Horus and Seth. Horus, the son of Osiris, the dead king, needs to avenge his father's death and also to secure for himself the throne left vacant by Osiris. Seth, the murderer, seeks to avoid his fate and at the same time outwit Horus and gain the throne.

This theme is elaborated into an extended literary composition in a text preserved on a fine papyrus in the Chester Beatty Library in Dublin. (This papyrus dates from about 1158 B.C.) The familiar way in which the gods are treated in this text is quite unusual, the resulting narrative having the character far more of the mythological tales of classical Greece than the pedestrian legends of Egyptian religion. Here the gods are seen to behave in a less than divine manner; they are almost caricatured. They are certainly not the mysterious deities who march through the reliefs on the walls of the temples of Egypt.

A typical ancient Egyptian papyrus roll.

The Contendings of Horus and Seth

The judging between Horus and Seth happened in this way. To argue their claims, the two gods appeared before Re-Herakhty, the Master of the Universe, as the great sun-god Re was known in one of his many forms of worship. Horus was still a small child. First Shu, the son of Re, spoke, addressing the great god: 'Justice should triumph; say that the throne should be given to Horus.' Thoth then added his support, speaking to the company of nine gods: 'That claim is a million times right!' and Isis, the mother of Horus, naturally joined in on the side of her son. So did the company of nine gods. But Re-Herakhty was not convinced.

Then Seth spoke up. 'Let Horus be sent out with me so that the company of gods can see how I can beat him.' Thoth disputed his suggestion, pointing out that the throne of Osiris could hardly be given to Seth while the son of Osiris still lived.

At this demonstration in favor of Horus, Re-Herakhty was furious, for he wanted Seth to succeed Osiris as king. 'What can we do?' asked Onuris, one of Horus' supporters. 'Let us get Banebdedet, the great goat-god of Mendes, to decide between the claims of these two contenders,' said the sun god.

When Banebdedet had come and was asked to decide the issue, he advised them to write to the goddess Neith, the mother of Re, who would know what to do. 'We ought not to do anything in ignorance,' he counseled. The company of nine gods saw the sense of this advice and called upon Thoth, the divine scribe, to write a letter to Neith.

So Thoth composed a carefully worded letter couched in formal language, in the name of Re-Herakhty. The crucial message ran as follows: 'I am much troubled in mind. I lie awake every night with no hope of sleep, considering the problem of Osiris' successor; and every day I take counsel with the Two Lands trying to resolve the issue. What are we to do about these two young men who have been pressing their claims before the divine council for the last eighty years? Nobody knows how to judge between them. Please write and tell us what to do.'

By return Neith wrote back to the company of nine gods advising them to give the throne to Horus. 'Refrain from committing those wicked deeds that are wholly out of place in these circumstances. If you fail to do so I shall be extremely angry, and the sky will come crashing down.' Neith proposed that they should formally approach Re-Herakhty and suggest that Seth should be compensated for the loss of the throne by having his possessions doubled and by awarding him Anat and Astarte, two attractive foreign goddesses who were daughters of Re. 'Place Horus in Osiris' seat,' she said.

When the letter was read out, the nine gods shouted approval at the judgment. But Re-Herakhty was furious and taunted Horus, saying that he was too weak to occupy his father's throne: 'Your body is feeble and royal position is far too great for you to sustain, you callow youth, whose mouth tastes badly!'

This attack annoyed the other gods intensely and one, named Babai, forgot himself enough to insult the Master of the Universe. 'Your shrine is neglected!' he sneered, implying that nobody paid much attention to him any longer.

Re-Herakhty was mightily hurt by this jibe, and he flung himself on the ground in anger, while the other gods turned on Babai and scolded him for being so rude. 'Be off with you! You have committed a real crime in saying this of Re.' So Babai was sent away, Re retired to his arbor to nurse his

hurt, and the other gods went to their tents to wait for an improvement in tempers.

In the end it was Hathor who saved the situation. She was a handsome goddess and knew her father's weakness. So she slipped into his arbor, stripped off her clothes, and flaunted her charms before him. Re-Herakhty laughed aloud at this performance and recovered his good humor. Coming forth from his arbor he called together the council of gods once more and ordered Horus and Seth to argue their cases themselves.

First Seth spoke: 'I am Seth, the strongest of the company of nine gods. Every day I slay the enemies of Re, and no other god can do this. I deserve the throne of Osiris.' Some of the gods cried, 'Seth is in the right.' But other gods defended Horus, and they began quarreling among themselves. 'It is quite intolerable,' said Onuris and Thoth together, 'that this high office should be given to a brother on the mother's side while a son of the body of the former holder of the office is still alive.' The opposite view was taken by Banebdedet, the great goat-god of Mendes, who

refused to be convinced that such an important position should be held by a young lad, while Seth, the elder brother, was still alive. His statement of the case was shouted down by the nine gods who thought it quite unworthy coming from such an important god.

Then Horus spoke: 'It is quite wrong that I should be tricked before the company of nine gods and that the throne of my father Osiris be taken away from me.'

The equivocal attitude of the nine gods made Isis angry on Horus' behalf, and she swore a mighty oath that she would obtain justice for him. The nine tried to calm her down with promises that justice would be done for the rightful claimant. Seth, however, took great offense at Isis' intervention and threatened the tribunal with violence. 'I shall take up my weighty staff and slay you all, one a day, until you all are dead.' And Seth swore that he would take no further part in the debate as long as Isis remained a member of the tribunal. So Re said to the gathering: 'Cross over to the island in the middle of the water, and instruct Anty, the divine ferryman, to refuse passage to Isis or anyone like her.'

When the gods had crossed over to the island, they settled down to a meal, and Anty, the ferryman, returned to the other side of the water. Shortly afterward Isis came near, disguised as an old woman; she walked with bent back, and she had a little gold ring on her hand. 'Take me across to the island, will you?' she said to Anty. 'I bring this pot of flour for the young boy who has spent five days on the island tending cattle; he is hungry.' Anty replied, 'I was given strict instructions to ferry no woman.' 'Was it because of Isis?' asked the goddess. But Anty ignored the question and asked her what she would give him.

At first Isis offered him a loaf of bread, but he rejected it scornfully. 'What means a loaf to me? Should I ferry you across to the island in the water just for a little loaf when I have been strictly commanded to ferry across no woman?' Isis was then obliged to offer Anty the gold ring she wore on her finger; with this great inducement she succeeded in overcoming his scruples and he agreed to take her across.

When they reached the island, Isis thanked Anty for his help and, leaving the boat, made her way through the trees toward the nine gods. Soon she could see them sitting in a leafy place eating a meal with the Master of the Universe. Seth looked in her direction as she came through the trees. But Isis, fearing to be recognized, and at the same time hoping to trick him, turned herself into an outstandingly beautiful woman, the like of whom was not to be found anywhere in the whole land.

As soon as he saw her, Seth was struck with a great desire, and he left the company of the other gods to pursue her. (Isis could be seen by none of the other gods.) Coming up close to Isis, Seth placed himself behind a tree and called out, 'I am here beside you, fair woman!' Coyly Isis answered: 'O my great lord, do me no wrong; I am in great distress. I was the wife of a cowherd and I bore him a son. While the boy was still young, his father died and, as was proper, he went to take control of his father's herd. At the very moment a stranger turned up who, sitting at ease in the barn, calmly told my son that he would beat him, turn him out of his house, and take over control of the herd. That now is the situation. My son is disinherited. Will you act for me on his behalf?'

When Seth heard this sad story, he was overcome with indignation: 'Shall the cattle be given to a stranger while the father's son is still alive?'

As he spoke these words Isis flew up into a tree as a kite and shouted to him, 'Your own sense has judged yourself!' And Seth realized how he had been tricked. He rushed off to Re and told him what had happened, blaming Anty for his predicament. So Anty was brought and had the soles of his feet removed; from that day on, he declared that he would never touch gold again.

Meanwhile the company of nine gods crossed to the eastern edge of the land, and there they received a message from Re, the great god, instructing them to install Horus in the place of Osiris. As they prepared to carry out this instruction, Seth objected in very forceful terms and swore that he and Horus should fight together in the water. Re agreed to this, and Seth said to Horus, 'Let us become two hippopotamuses and fight in the water. He who survives three months shall receive the throne.'

When the two were in the water, Isis could not resist interfering again.

She prepared a harpoon on a cord and flung it into the water. First she struck Horus, and then she struck Seth. But she failed to follow up her advantage, and took pity on Seth when he reminded her of their kinship. When Horus saw her release the barb from Seth, he lost his temper, rushed out of the water with his sixteen-pound cleaver, and chopped off her head. He put it into his bosom and stalked up into the mountains.

Isis then turned herself into a headless flint statue. When Re-Herakhty saw it, he asked Thoth, 'Who is this woman who comes here and has no head?' When Thoth explained that it was Isis and that her own son Horus had struck off her head, the great god was beyond himself with anger and called out the nine gods to start in pursuit immediately: 'Let us find Horus and punish him severely for what he has done.' At once the nine gods set out toward the hills to track down Horus, who had in the meantime laid himself down to rest beneath a tree in a small grove.

It was Seth who first came upon him. Without giving Horus a chance, he leapt on him, threw him on his back, tore out both his eyes and buried them in the ground. Here they took root, becoming two corms; eventually two lotus flowers sprang up from them. On his return to Re, Seth pretended not to have found Horus.

Horus, who had been left sightless and weeping in the desert, was found by Hathor. She took milk from a gazelle and restored his sight by anointing his eye sockets with it. She then brought Horus back to the tribunal and told the gods what had happened. 'Call Horus and Seth here for judgment,' said the nine. Re-Herakhty then pronounced judgment on them: 'Pay attention to what I say. Go and feast together. Be at peace, and stop quarreling all the time.' So Seth invited Horus to his house, and Horus agreed.

When evening came, a bed was prepared, and the two gods lay down together. During the night Seth made an assault on Horus, but Horus was ready and caught Seth's

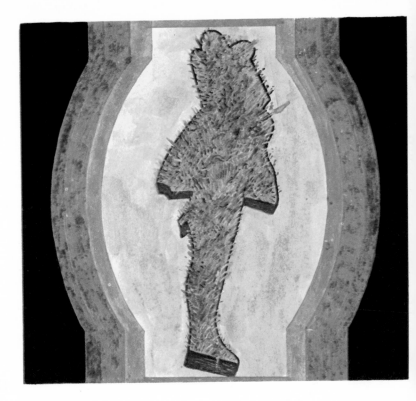

seed and rushed off to Isis, saying, 'O mother! Look what Seth has done to me.' She was shocked and immediately took her knife, cut off his hand, and threw it into the water, replacing it with another. She then took a sample of Horus' seed and carried it to Seth's garden. Seeking out Seth's gardener, Isis asked him which plants Seth usually ate. 'Of all the plants that grow here,' he answered, 'Seth only eats lettuce.' When he had shown her which plants they were, she sprinkled the seed on them. Shortly afterward Seth came into the garden, as he did every day, and he ate the lettuce just as the gardener had said. And he became pregnant with Horus' seed.

After a little time Seth suggested to Horus that they should go again before the tribunal to put their cases. As soon as they were in the presence of the gods Seth began vaunting his own prowess, and he won over the nine gods. But Horus laughed aloud and asked the gods to call on their

respective seeds to see from where they would answer. Thoth put his hand on Horus and invoked the seed of Seth; it answered from the marsh. He then put his hand on Seth and invoked the seed of Horus; it answered from Seth. Thoth said, 'Come out onto the forehead of Seth.' It appeared like a golden sun there. Seth was furious and would have thrown it down, but Thoth took it and placed it on his own head.

Next, Seth challenged Horus to a combat in boats. First Horus made a boat of cedar and plastered it on the outside. Its appearance deceived Seth, who thought it was made of stone; so he cut himself a stone boat. When the two boats were launched, Seth's boat sank immediately, so he changed himself into a hippopotamus and overturned Horus' boat. Then Horus aimed a harpoon at Seth, but the nine gods restrained him, saying, 'Don't throw it at him!'

At this, Horus packed up his harpoon in his boat and went

off to Sais to ask the goddess Neith to intervene once more in their eighty-year-old dispute. 'Let judgment now at last be made between me and Seth,' he begged. 'For eighty years we have lingered in the tribunal, and no one knows any better now than at the beginning how to decide between us. And yet he has never been judged right, while I have won the day a thousand times. He never pays any attention to anything the nine gods say to him.'

When the nine heard Horus' complaint, they agreed with what he said. Thoth then said to Re-Herakhty, 'Why not write to Osiris and ask for his opinion?' 'How right Thoth is!' said Shu. So Re instructed Thoth to write to Osiris to learn what he advised: 'Tell us,' he wrote, 'what we should do with Horus and Seth? For we do not want to act in ignorance.'

The letter took many days to reach Osiris, the king. When it had been read out to him he exploded with annoyance and addressed an answer without delay to Re-Herakhty: 'Why should Horus be cheated? Is it not I who make you strong?

Is it not I who make the barley and the wheat that feed the gods and all other living creatures after the gods? Is there any god or goddess who is able to do the same?'

This letter reached Re-Herakhty while he sat with the nine gods; when it had been read out to him he immediately dictated an answer: 'And what if you had never come into existence? The food would still be here without you.' In reply Osiris wrote: 'Everything you have done is good, you maker of the nine gods; but justice has been allowed to go down to the underworld. I have many savage-faced emissaries here whom I could send out to bring back the hearts of those who do wrong. What does my being here mean? I am stronger than you. When Ptah made the sky, he told the stars that every night they would sleep in the West where Osiris is; and after them, all other people will rest with Osiris.'

When that letter had reached Re-Herakhty and had been read out, the nine gods cried out, 'Everything the great lord of plenty says is right.' Then Seth suggested that they should all go again to the island in the middle of the water to settle the matter once and for all. So they crossed the water once more, and in conclave they declared Horus the victor. The great god then ordered Isis to bring Seth fettered before the gods, and when he had come he asked him. 'Why have you not allowed this matter to be decided against you, but have assumed for yourself the throne of Osiris?' 'Not at all,' said Seth. 'Let Horus be called and given the throne of his father Osiris.'

So Horus was brought and installed on his father's throne. 'And what shall be done with Seth now?' enquired Ptah. 'Let him come to me,' answered Re-Herakhty, and he can thunder in the heavens and terrify men.' He then ordered the nine gods to praise Horus and prostrate themselves before him. Isis set the example, and the earth rejoiced when they saw Horus, the son of Isis, established in the office of his father Osiris.

MYTH AND FOLKTALE IN HUMAN ACTIONS

In the last story the characters are all gods, and no pretense is made that the events related are anything but mythical. The gods behave like humans, but their actions are divine and conform to no natural laws. In this next story, the situation is somewhat different. The tale unfolds as if it concerns ordinary human beings engaged in the simple tasks of the Egyptian countryside. But quite early on there are hints that one of the characters is far from being a simple Egyptian peasant. He is described as having a divine element in his make-up, and he is soon revealed as one who possesses remarkable gifts. Both he and his brothers have names that belong to Egyptian gods. Anpu is Anubis, best known as the god of embalming. Bata is a little-known god of great antiquity who belonged to none of the great companies of gods worshipped in the important centers in Egypt. Bata's shrine was at Sako in Middle Egypt across the river Nile from Hardai, where there was a shrine of Anubis. A local rivalry between these deities in Middle Egypt is probably reflected in the theme of this story, but its significance is obscure. The advantage ultimately lies with Bata, but Anpu emerges far more creditably than might have been expected from the inauspicious beginning. It has been interpreted as a myth involving the rivalry of these gods but transferred to the realm of human activities. And in addition to the mythical elements, there are elements from folktales. One such is the removal of the heart—representing the desire to preserve a person's vital self against his enemies: this is a traditional motif in the folklore of various lands. In the end, though, we need not worry too much about searching for hidden meanings; as did most Egyptians, we may take it as just a good story. This fine tale exists today in only one form, a papyrus roll known as the 'Orbiney Papyrus' (after a former owner). Now in the British Museum, it is complete and well preserved and dates from about 1210 B.C. As with most Egyptian manuscripts, the story itself is probably much older.

The Tale of the Two Brothers

Once there were two brothers. The elder was named Anpu and the younger, Bata. Anpu was married and had a farm in which he lived with his wife; he also looked after Bata and treated him as his son. In return Bata did everything to help Anpu; he made his clothes, he drove his cattle to pasture, he plowed Anpu's fields, harvested his crops, and did all that had to be done. Bata was a handsome youth, unsurpassed in beauty in the neighborhood; there was something quite divine about him, as if he had been touched by god. Every day he went about his business in the fields, and in the evenings he returned to Anpu's house, bringing crops in season for the kitchen, milk from the cows, fodder for the animals around the farm, firewood and straw for heating and

bedding. Each night Bata laid his tribute before his brother while he sat with his wife eating their evening meal. Bata took no part in their domestic life but withdrew to the cowshed where he made his bed among the cattle.

Every morning Bata got up early and prepared his brother's breakfast. Anpu usually handed him his provisions for the day and sent him off to his labors. Bata, however, had a rare understanding of the cattle, and he relied on them to tell him where the best grazing was. As they left the farm in the morning, they would say, 'The grass is especially good in this meadow, or in that meadow,' and he took them wherever they advised. Consequently they thrived greatly; they grew into fine beasts and calved unusually well.

When the season of cultivation came round, Anpu told Bata: 'You'd better get a good pair of oxen ready for the plowing; for the waters of the Nile-flood have now gone down, and the land is in the right condition for working. Make sure you have plenty of seed. Tomorrow we'll have to start plowing.' Bata noted what his brother said, and before he went to bed that

night he made ready all that would be needed the next day. He measured out the seed and gave the oxen special attention so that they could make an early start.

Next morning at sunrise Anpu and Bata went off together with the oxen and the seed. It was a fine, crisp morning, and the work went well; they enjoyed their labor and were happy. So quickly did the work progress that they ran out of seed, and Anpu sent Bata back to the village to fetch more. Bata went back to the farm where he found his sister-in-law sitting in the shade outside the house, combing her hair and applying her cosmetics. 'Get up and go and get me some more seed,' he said, 'We need more in our work, and my brother is waiting for me to get back. Don't keep me hanging about.'

'Certainly not!' said the woman. 'You go to the granary and get what you want. You don't expect me to stop my hairdressing, do you?'

Bata went off meekly to the granary with a large container that he filled with the seed they needed. When he came out of the granary, the woman saw him, bearing his load easily

and looking remarkably strong and handsome. 'How much is that load you have on your shoulder?' she called out.

'About three measures of wheat and two measures of barley,' said Bata.

Anpu's wife had never paid much attention to Bata in the past, but suddenly she saw him for what he was, and a great desire took hold of her. So she kept him chatting, praising his beauty and admiring his strength. Then she took hold of him, saying, 'Come inside with me for a time, and let us make love together. I'll see that all will be well for you, and I'll make you fine clothes.' But Bata would have none of this. He turned on her in fury, reminding her that she was like a mother to him. 'Never mention it again,' he said, 'and I'll tell nobody what has happened.' He took up his load, returned to his brother and continued in the work.

Throughout the day the work went well, and by the time evening came Anpu and Bata had together accomplished more than they had hoped. When the light became too poor to work, Anpu returned to his house, leaving his younger brother to bring back the plowing team and the produce of the fields as he always did. He also collected together his cattle to drive them back to the cowshed for the night.

In the meanwhile Anpu's wife had had time to reflect on what had passed between her and Bata in the morning, and she realized that she had been very foolish. She was terrified that Bata might have spoken to Anpu about her advances. Attack seemed the best method of defense to her, so she smothered herself with fat, pretending that she had been beaten, and she drank oil to make herself sick. She would tell her husband that Bata had beaten her during the morning.

As was customary, Anpu reached home first and was surprised to find his wife in a terrible state, lying down on her bed, groaning as if she had been beaten, and vomiting. She did not meet him at the door of the house as she usually did, bearing a pot of water to pour over his hands and a lighted lamp to help him find his way indoors. Groping his way into the house, Anpu found her in her sad state. 'Who has been speaking to you?' he asked. 'No one,' she answered, 'except your younger brother. When he came to get more seed this morning he found me sitting alone and suggested that we should spend an hour lying together. Of course I did not listen to him, but I reminded him that I was like a mother to him, while you were like his father. He then lost his nerve and beat me to keep me quiet. If you let him live after this, I shall surely kill myself. But do not wait to question him on his return, for if he is faced with my charges he will surely pervert them into a hurt against himself.'

When he heard this tale, Anpu lost all control of himself. He grabbed his spear and took up a position behind the door of the cowshed to wait for Bata's return. After some time, along came Bata with the cattle, bringing produce from the fields in his normal way. As the first cow entered the shed it said, 'Look out, Bata! Your brother stands here with his spear, waiting to kill you.' The second cow gave the same warning, and when Bata saw Anpu's feet showing beneath the door of the shed, he dropped his burden and ran away as fast as he could, with Anpu chasing behind him, brandishing his spear.

As he ran, Bata prayed aloud to the great god Re-Herakhty:

A heart amulet from an Egyptian papyrus.
A faience drinking cup. About 1000 B.C. British Museum.

'My good lord, help me! For thou art the one who judges between the wrong-doer and the just man!' The god heard his prayer and in answer laid down a stretch of water, teeming with crocodiles, between the two brothers. Anpu stood on the far shore beating his hands together in fury. Bata shouted to him, 'Wait until dawn, when judgment will be made between us. Yet I shall never live with you again. I go to the Valley of the Cedar.'

When morning came, Bata saw his brother on the other side of the water and shouted to him: 'Why did you pursue me with your spear before you heard my story? After all, I am your younger brother, and you and your wife have been like a father and mother to me. Yesterday when I went home to get more seed, your wife tried to seduce me, but I refused to do anything with her and she has now turned the facts against me.' Bata told his brother everything that had happened and swore by Re-Herakhty: 'What you have done to harm me has been at the request of a whore.' He then took a knife and cut off

his penis and threw it into the water where a fish swallowed it. Bata fell at once fainting to the ground and his brother, realizing the wrong he had done, felt full of guilt and very sorry; but he was unable to cross the water to Bata because of the crocodiles, and he stood on the far bank weeping and wringing his hands. Then Bata called out to Anpu again and begged him in return for any good he had done him in the past to help in the future: 'You will know when there is something wrong with me for I shall take my heart and place it on the flower of a cedar. If it falls, come and seek it, and continue the search no matter how long it takes. When you find it, place it in water and it will revive and take vengeance for me. You will know that something is wrong when your mug of beer foams. When that happens, come at once. And it will certainly happen.'

Then Anpu went home in sadness, slew his wife, and threw her body to his dogs. He dwelt in mourning for his younger brother.

Meanwhile Bata reached the Valley of the Cedar and made

his home there, spending his days hunting in the desert. One day as he emerged from the castle he had built, he met the company of nine gods who told him what Anpu had done. They were sorry for Bata, and Re-Herakhty, the chief god, told Khnum, the god who fashioned men, to make a wife to comfort him. This he did, producing a wonderful woman compounded of divine elements. But the Seven Hathors, who knew the fate of all creatures, warned, 'She will suffer a nasty death.'

Bata loved her greatly and hunted daily for her. He warned her never to go out, and to beware of the sea: 'I cannot save you for I am a woman like you.' And he told her about his heart: 'It lies on the top of the flower of the cedar and if anybody discovers it, I shall have to fight with him.'

One day, however, Bata's wife went out walking and was pursued by the sea, which begged the cedar to catch her. The cedar stole a lock from her hair for the sea, which then carried it to Egypt, depositing it at the spot where Pharaoh's washermen worked. The smell of the hair pervaded Pharaoh's clothes and his servants complained to the washermen who were much troubled. The dispute between the servants and the washermen continued for many days, and the chief washerman became very depressed. After one of the daily wrangles he went for a walk along the river bank to consider the matter quietly. By chance he stopped at the very spot where the lock of hair lay in the water. He sent a man down to retrieve it, and when he examined it he found it had a very sweet smell. So he took it to Pharaoh who sought the advice of his wise men. They told him: 'This lock belongs to a daughter of Re-Herakhty, who contains the elements of all gods. It must be a gift from a distant land. Send messengers to all lands to find her; but send especially to the Valley of the Cedar.' The messengers were sent forthwith.

After some time, all the messengers returned except those who had gone to the Valley of the Cedar; for Bata had killed all of them, sparing only one to report to Pharaoh. So His Majesty then sent a great force of soldiers to bring back Bata's wife, and with the soldiers he sent a woman bearing all kinds of jewelry and garments. They took her without trouble, and brought her back to Egypt amid great rejoicing. His Majesty fell in love with her at once and called her Chief

Favorite. But he feared the vengeance of Bata and asked the woman to describe her husband. So she advised His Majesty, 'Get them to cut down the cedar and break it up.' He sent soldiers back again to cut down the tree and this they did, felling the tree with the flower that bore Bata's heart. At that moment Bata fell down dead.

The next day when Anpu, Bata's brother, returned home and sat down, a mug of beer was brought to him and it foamed. They then brought him a mug of wine, and this had turned sour. At once he dressed for a journey, took up his weapons and set out for the Valley of the Cedar. When he arrived he entered his brother's castle and found him lying dead. He wept to see him so, but he remembered his words of long ago and went out to search for the heart as Bata had begged. For three years he sought in vain, but when the fourth year began he longed for Egypt. On the evening before he had resolved to leave he searched once more and found the berry that was Bata's heart. He took it and placed it in a jar of water, and during that night it absorbed the water. Then Bata's body quivered and he looked at Anpu, who rushed to the jar and found that the berry had absorbed all the water and was transformed into Bata's heart. When

it had been replaced, Bata became himself again and the brothers embraced. 'I shall now become a great bull with strange markings,' said Bata, 'and you shall sit on my back, and we shall go and take vengeance on my wife. Take me to Pharaoh and you will be much rewarded, for I shall seem to be a great wonder in the land.'

When the following day dawned, Bata assumed the form of a bull, and taking Anpu on his back he reached Pharaoh's palace. When His Majesty heard about the bull he was delighted and kept him in the palace, giving much treasure to Anpu who then returned to his village. Some time later the bull approached the Chief Favorite. 'Behold! I still live,' he whispered. 'Who are you?' said she, wondering. He answered: 'I am Bata, and I know how you had the cedar cut down to get rid of me; but I am still alive.' She was terrified, and at the earliest opportunity, when she sat with Pharaoh, she said, 'Pray, grant whatever I may ask you.' And His Majesty agreed but was much upset when she asked to eat some of the bull's liver. He had, however, made his promise, and next day he declared a festival with the sacrifice of the bull. To carry out the sad deed Pharaoh sent one of his chief butchers; after the bull had been slaughtered, two drops of

blood fell to the ground by the doorposts of the Great Gateway of Pharaoh. From them sprang two sprouts that quickly developed into fine trees. When the people saw these trees they ran and told Pharaoh. The event was taken as an omen; there was great rejoicing, and His Majesty made an offering before them.

A little later, Pharaoh set out in his golden chariot to view the trees, and the Favorite came after him. His Majesty sat down beneath one of the trees, and his Favorite sat beneath the other. She had scarcely settled herself when her tree whispered: 'You betrayer! I am Bata. In spite of you I still live. I know exactly how you arranged to have the cedar cut down for Pharaoh because of me. And when I became a bull you had me slaughtered.'

The Favorite waited until a good opportunity presented itself. Then one day, as she entertained Pharaoh, pouring wine for him and making him content, she said, 'Pray, grant whatever I may ask you.' His Majesty agreed, and she asked, 'Have the two trees cut down and made into fine furniture.' Again Pharaoh did what she wanted and sent for his cleverest carpenters. While they worked, Pharaoh and his Favorite

stood watching; as they watched, a tiny chip of wood flew up from an ax and it entered the Favorite's mouth. Involuntarily she swallowed it, and soon she became pregnant. Meanwhile the king arranged for the trees to be made into fine furniture as she wished.

After a time, the Favorite gave birth to a boy and her attendants told Pharaoh the good news. From the very first, he loved the child and honored him by appointing him Viceroy of Kush. Later on, when he had grown, the child was made Crown Prince of the land. He held this rank for many years until the old king died. Immediately the new king commanded: 'Summon together all my highest officials so that I can tell them everything that has happened to me.' In their presence, and with his old wife by his side, Bata (for that is who he was) told them his story, and they judged between their new Pharaoh and his wife to her disadvantage.

Having at last secured his vengeance, Bata summoned Anpu to court and appointed him Crown Prince of the land. For thirty years, Bata ruled Egypt as Pharaoh, and when he passed to the better life Anpu became king.

A MORALITY TALE

Two brothers named Truth and Falsehood are the protagonists in this story of jealousy and retribution, which represents the struggle between good and evil as the ancient Egyptians envisaged it. The moral aspects of the struggle are more complicated than is implied by the simple confrontation of truth and falsehood in modern terms. In Egyptian terms, the idea embodied in the word *maat* which, for want of a better single word (and for historical reasons) is usually translated by 'truth,' contains the element of 'order' as well as that of veracity. A situation involving *maat* was one that conformed properly to the divine order; it was right, just, true, constituted according to what gods and men thought to be best for the satisfactory running of life. *Gereg*, 'falsehood,' was the antithesis of *maat*, and in this story the conflict between the two ideas is quite explicitly demonstrated. The one document that preserves the tale—dating from about 1200 B.C.—has various omissions, but the intended course of the story is clear.

Truth and Falsehood

It would seem that at some time Truth had borrowed a knife from his brother, and when the moment came to return it, he found that he had lost it. With much apology he explained the loss to Falsehood, promising to make it good with another knife. The replacement was rejected by Falsehood who with unreasonable fury claimed that the missing knife was unique: 'Its blade consists of the mountain of El, its handle is the wood of Coptos, its sheath is the tomb of the god, and its thongs are the cattle of Kar.' Quite determined to exact what he considered to be a proper recompense from his brother, Falsehood insisted on a legal judgment and brought Truth before a court presided over by the company of nine gods. His motives in taking this drastic action were inspired by a deep-seated hatred; he hoped not only to exact retribution for the harm done to him in the loss of his knife, but also to hurt Truth so fundamentally

The golden dagger of Tutankhamon. About 1350 B.C. Cairo Museum.

that he would be no trouble to him in the future. Falsehood presented his case in the court and demanded: 'Have Truth brought here and strike out his two eyes. Let him be the doorkeeper of my house.' The evidence was presented and, as Truth in his honesty had no defense to offer, the court found him guilty and had to concede the punishment demanded by Falsehood.

Some days later, after Truth had been blinded and installed as the doorkeeper in his brother's house, Falsehood looked at him, realizing that although he had obtained his revenge, he could never escape the feeling of guilt that Truth's constant presence would arouse. So he called two of Truth's old servants and ordered them to take their former master into the desert and throw him to a fierce lion and its lionesses.

The two servants led Truth away to the desert hills where the lion was said to lurk. As they went, Truth begged them not to carry out their evil deed, but to leave him to his fate among the rocks. Perhaps strangers would find him and take him far away from the malevolence of Falsehood. Much touched by their former master's appeal, the two servants did as he requested, leaving him alive among the rocks and returning to Falsehood to report that they had carried out his orders.

Although Truth had been left in a place where he might have been found by strangers passing through the district, no one came near him. In his helplessness he wandered off the path and lost his way among the rocks of the hillside. After some days, his little stock of food and water exhausted, he lay down in weakness and hunger in the shadow of a small outcrop and fell asleep. As he lay there, a lady passed by, taking the air in the cool of the day. She was at once struck by his remarkable beauty in spite of his disheveled and filthy condition; she thought there could not be anyone as handsome as he in the whole land. When she reached her house, she instructed some of her man-servants to go up into the desert and bring back the man she had seen lying there. He would suit very nicely as the doorkeeper of her house. When they had returned with Truth, the lady of the house told them to bring him to her. Although he was blind and still showed the marks of his trials in the desert, when she saw him she felt a great desire stir in herself, for in all his body he was beautiful. That night he came to her in her room and made love with her.

In due course, the lady gave birth to a son of exceptional qualities. As a baby, he was finer than any other baby in the land; he was like a divine child. As a young man, he excelled his fellows in all he did. At school he worked hard, and he became a first-class scribe; in the field he practiced the military skills and again showed himself superior to his companions. But his success made him unpopular; his companions teased him, asking, 'Who is your father?' And when he could not answer, they said, 'You certainly have no father.' He bore their jibes for a time, but in the end he went in desperation to his mother and asked her to tell him: 'I am teased to distraction by my friends who say I have no father; please tell me who he is so that I can satisfy their curiosity and stop them worrying me.' She then pointed out the blind man at the door and said: 'See that man yonder. He is your father.' This answer shocked the young man, and he took the blind man into the house and did what he could for him. He placed him comfortably in a chair, set a

stool beneath his feet, and brought him food and drink.
'Who blinded you?' he asked. 'Tell me so that I can avenge
you.' 'It was my young brother,' answered his father. When
the whole story had been told, the son set off to seek vengeance, taking ten loaves, a staff, a pair of sandals, a waterskin, and a sword. He also obtained a fine ox, and made his
way to Falsehood's herdsman. He found him in the pastures
tending Falsehood's herd and he approached him, saying:
'Good man, I have to go into the town for some days, but
cannot take this ox with me. Would you kindly tend it for me
until I return?' 'What will you give me if I do so?' asked the
herdsman. 'These things that I carry,' said the young man.
The herdsman readily agreed and took the loaves, the staff,
the sandals, waterskin, and sword, while Truth's son went
into the town, leaving the ox in Falsehood's pastures.

After some months, Falsehood went to inspect his herd
and immediately took a fancy to the fine ox. 'Have that

splendid beast prepared for me to eat,' he instructed his
herdsman. 'That I cannot do,' said the other, 'for it is not part
of your herd. I am looking after it for a young man.' 'Don't
worry about that,' said Falsehood. 'Give him one of mine
instead; there are plenty in my herd.'

When Truth's son heard that his ox had been taken, he
returned to claim it from the herdsman. 'Where is my fine
ox? I cannot see it among your herd.' 'Don't worry about
your ox,' said the herdsman. 'Take any one of these in the
herd in its place.' But the boy protested: 'Where is there an
ox as large as my ox? If it were to stand at Balamun, its tail
would reach to the edge of the Delta. One horn would rest on
the western hills and one on the eastern hills. The great
river is its resting place, and sixty calves are born to it every
day.' In disbelief, the herdsman denied that such an ox could
exist. So the boy seized him and led him off to Falsehood, con-
fronting him with what he had done to his ox. He then took
Falsehood himself before the company of nine gods.

After Truth's son had made his accusation, the gods said: 'You are wrong. We have never seen an ox as big as that.' At once the boy rejoined: 'And where have you seen such a knife as you claim has a blade that is the mountain of El, a handle that is the wood of Coptos, a sheath that is the tomb of the god, and thongs that are the cattle of Kar? Judge therefore between Truth and Falsehood, for I am Truth's son, and I have come to avenge him.'

At that Falsehood swore, 'As Amun and Prince endure, if Truth can be found alive, let me be blinded and made the doorkeeper of his house!'

In reply the boy swore, 'As Amun and the Prince endure, if Truth be found alive, let Falsehood be severely punished with blows and wounds. And let him be blinded in both his eyes, and make him serve as the doorkeeper in Truth's house!'

And so it happened, and Falsehood met the fate he had himself planned for Truth. The boy had avenged his father and brought the dispute between Truth and Falsehood to a just ending.

A STORY ON STONE

Within the enclosure walls of all the great temples built in Egypt during the late period, down to the times when the Roman emperors ruled the country, stand small buildings now called Mammisis, or Birth Houses. The Birth House is an independent chamber of simple form decorated with reliefs that deal with the birth of Pharaoh, showing it to have been divinely conceived. From the earliest times, the king was thought of as a god and as the son of god. One of his regular titles was 'Son of Re'. When the kingship was settled and the succession ran smoothly, this fiction of the divine origin was quite acceptable. But in different times, when the claim to the throne of any particular king was questionable, it was especially important to emphasize that his claim

Queen Hatshepsut shown as a king. About 1480 B.C. Metropolitan Museum.

Hatshepsut's mortuary temple at Deir el-Bahri. About 1490 B.C.

derived from the nature of his birth and the divinity of his
father. The regular building of Birth Houses in late temples
shows that by then it had become a necessity to demonstrate
pictorially this divine paternity.

During the 18th Dynasty, the great imperial period of
Egypt's history, two monarchs found it advisable to decorate
parts of temples with reliefs commemorating their divine
conceptions and births. These were Queen Hatshepsut and
King Amenophis III. The sequence of events in what was
represented as the true story of the queen's birth is shown in
reliefs in the terraced mortuary temple of Hatshepsut at
Deir el-Bahri, built about 1490 B.C. To judge from other
reliefs in the temple, the figures in the birth scenes were
delineated with a certain stiffness characteristic of the royal
art of the period. The actual carving was crisp and sure with
a great deal of sensitive modeling in the representation of
heads and limbs The color with which they were originally

The Birth House of the temple at Dendera. First century B.C.

painted was brilliant, but little of it now remains.

After Hatshepsut had been succeeded by her nephew Tuthmosis III, a campaign was initiated to remove the memory of the queen from her visible monuments throughout Egypt. It is not certain whether Hatshepsut died before Tuthmosis recovered the throne, which he considered his aunt had usurped. It is possible that he returned to power as the result of a palace revolt and that Hatshepsut was deposed and kept in relative custody until she died. Her death would have provided the opportunity for expunging her memory, and one of the principal targets for attack would have been the scenes and texts that extolled her divine birth and justified her claim to the throne. The agents of the king systematically trimmed away the reliefs and inscriptions, chiseling carefully around the outlines of the carvings. When they had finished, the walls bore, as it were, shadows of what had been there originally, so that the scenes can be followed without much difficulty. The texts that accompany them, unfortunately, are more seriously damaged, but what remains can be supplemented to some extent by the record surviving in the temple of Amenophis III at Luxor.

The Divine Birth of Hatshepsut

In the first scene, the great god Amon-Re, Lord of the Thrones of the Two Lands, is shown in conference with the Council of Nine Gods. They have been summoned to discuss the question of the next ruler for Egypt. Amon-Re declares his intention to father the new ruler, who is already given Hatshepsut's name, and he promises to ensure her sovereign might over all lands. The gods, it seems, willingly concur in his plans, and the stage is set for the divine seduction of the queen, the chief wife of the ruling king.

For the purpose of meeting his prospective bride, the god is assisted by Thoth, the divine scribe and master of knowledge. Thoth identifies her as Aahmes: 'She is more beautiful than any other woman in the land, and she is the wife of the King of Upper and Lower Egypt. He is Tuthmosis, and is still a young man. You should go to her.' Thoth then leads Amon-

Re to Aahmes, and the relief shows the god seated side by side with the queen on a bed supported by two protecting goddesses. Amon-Re describes how he took the outer form of the queen's husband, Tuthmosis I, so as to gain easy access to her bedchamber. In his counterfeit form he passed the guards of the queen's apartments and confidently slipped through the anteroom where the queen's maidservants watched. In the bedchamber he found the queen fast asleep on her bed, beautiful in form and very desirable to him. As the divine fragrance of the god reached her, she awoke. Half asleep, she saw the figure before her and recognized it as the king, her husband, and she welcomed him into her bed. He lay with her as he desired and accomplished what he wanted . His deception had truly been successful, but his divine pride would not allow him to depart without telling the queen who he was. So he revealed himself to her as Amon-Re, King of the Gods, Lord of the Thrones of the Two Lands. Aahmes, divining his

purpose, accepted him and marveled at his beauty; his love passed into her limbs and the palace was filled with his sweet perfume. When he kissed her, she said: 'My lord, how great is your fame! How splendid it is to see your magnificence! You have joined my majesty with your glory, and your breath pervades my limbs.' The queen was wholly captivated by the charms of the god and submitted to him in all that he desired of her. At length he told her that in due time she would give birth. 'Hatshepsut will be the name of the daughter I have placed in your body. She will exercise the kingship over the whole land of Egypt. I shall give her my fame and my authority and my crown, and she will rule the Two Lands under my protection.'

When Amon-Re finally left the queen, he went straight to see Khnum, the god who had been entrusted with the making of man. 'Go now,' he said, 'and create this future ruler of Egypt. Make her and her spirit from my own limbs; and fashion her better than the gods, for I have given her all health and wealth and strength and happiness to live forever like the god Re. 'I shall do it immediately,' answered Khnum. 'She will seem more splendid than the gods themselves when she appears in glory as ruler of Egypt.'

In the scene that illustrates his act of creating the child, Khnum is shown seated behind a low, round-topped table that represents his potter's wheel. On the top of the table stand two tiny figures, both apparently male; one is to be Hatshepsut, and one her spirit. In front kneels the goddess Heqet, a frog-headed deity, who transmits life to the figures. As Khnum works he utters a suitable incantation: 'I create you from the limbs of Amon, the foremost one of Karnak. I have come to fashion you better than the gods. I give you all health and wealth and strength and happiness. I give you all lands and all peoples, all offerings and all food. I shall make you appear

in glory upon the throne of Horus, like the sun-god Re. I shall make you first among the living when you shine as ruler of Upper and Lower Egypt, just as your father Amon-Re commanded.'

Now that all had been satisfactorily arranged in preparation for the birth of Hatshepsut, Amon-Re sends Thoth as his messenger to visit Aahmes and invest her with marks of his favor in the form of special titles and epithets. In this way she will know that the great god is pleased with her and wishes her to be blessed with all forms of human happiness forever.

When the time approaches for the birth to take place, the gods again intervene to ensure that all will go as Amon-Re would wish. A special confinement chamber is prepared, and the two deities responsible for the creation of the child are sent to conduct the queen there. In the temple relief Aahmes is shown, discreetly pregnant, walking forward hand-in-hand

with Khnum, the ram-headed god, and Heqet, the frog-headed goddess. 'I invest your daughter with my protection,' says Khnum. 'You are great, but she who will spring from your womb will be greater than any king who has lived before.' As they advance they are joined by other attendant gods and, finally, by Amon-Re who leads the procession in its last stages to the confinement chamber.

On reaching the special room, Aahmes is handed over to the care of the presiding goddess of birth, Meskhent. She sits on a throne overlooking the room, and the confinement takes place on a great couch with lion legs. All the great and small deities whose functions include the care of mothers in childbirth and of newly born children are at hand. Isis and Nephthys are there. Also in the company are Bes, the gay, ugly, leonine dwarf who helps to drive away snakes and scorpions from children, and Thoeris, the benevolent hippopotamus goddess, herself pregnant, who comforts mothers in labor. With so much help and attention, Aahmes has no difficulty with the birth, and she is shown seated on a low-

backed chair, cradling the newly born Hatshepsut on her lap. The attending deities rejoice at the birth and hold out toward the child the gift of life, symbolized by its special hieroglyphic sign. Meskhent herself sanctifies the whole proceedings and bestows all health, wealth, strength, and

happiness on the royal child.

The next important step is to show the infant to her father, and for this task the goddess Hathor is chosen. Here she appears as a kindly goddess in the guise of a beautiful lady; she sits as she holds out Hatshepsut to Amon-Re. 'You are my own image,' he says, 'whom I have myself created. Be blessed, my child. You are a monarch who will reign over Egypt, seated on the throne of Horus.' He then takes the child from Hathor and holds her up before his face. 'Welcome, welcome, child of my own body. You are a monarch who will reign over Egypt and appear gloriously on the throne of Horus forever.'

Divine supervision over Hatshepsut does not end yet, for according to the mythical ideas surrounding the notion of divine birth, the child has to be properly launched into life and provided with all that she requires for a long and prosperous reign. In her earliest years, therefore, she is shown as being in the charge of gods especially qualified to rear her.

They look after the queen, Aahmes, and two of their number, represented with cow-heads, suckle Hatshepsut and her spirit. These are forms of the goddess Hathor, who is seen in the reliefs of Hatshepsut's temple at Deir el-Bahri as a cow suckling the queen. After they have been weaned, the child and its spirit are carried away by a god representing the Nile in flood, and by the god of milk, called Iat; together they symbolize nourishment and plenty. They present the two infant figures to seated gods. At this point in the development of the divine child, it is apparently necessary for Amon-Re to reassure himself that all continues to prosper with her. The young princess, therefore, is brought again into the presence of the great god by her divine nurses. This time Amon-Re is accompanied by Thoth who, as is proper for the gods, has taken a great deal of interest in the creation of Hatshepsut and in her upbringing. The king of the gods holds up the princess and her spirit and carefully inspects them. Once again she is invested with life and prosperity, strength, health and happiness, nourishment, and the promise that she may occupy the throne of Horus forever.

Aftermath of the Story

The final act in the story deals with the establishment of the length of Hatshepsut's reign. This important arrangement is in the hands of Anubis, the jackal-headed god who is more usually involved in the preparation of bodies for burial, and of Khnum, who very properly completes here his own act of creation. Anubis rolls forward a disk, which may represent the cycle of years, and he and Khnum individually bestow the usual benefits on the princess, adding millions of years and millions of jubilees on the throne of Horus. Their gift is sealed by the goddess Seshat, who notes down for the record this infinite length of reign.

So the pageant of Hatshepsut's conception and birth comes to an end.

As a pictorial way of demonstrating the divine right of a particular monarch to sit on the throne of Egypt, the carvings at Deir el-Bahri seem to have had no earlier parallel. But the idea and the purpose were very important, and so the series was repeated just under a hundred years later by the Pharaoh Amenophis III in the Luxor temple.

HISTORICAL INSCRIPTION—OR FICTION?

A little to the south of Aswan in the middle of the Nile, among the rocks of the First Cataract, is an island called Siheil. It is littered with granite boulders that offered very convenient surfaces for the inscriptions left by ancient Egyptian officials whose work took them to the cataract region and south into Nubia. Most of the texts are quite short and record simply the passage of an expedition; some commemorate royal visits. Some texts are votive in character, containing short prayers to the deities of the cataract region, to Khnum, Anukis, and Satis, who are often represented receiving offerings from officials and kings. Others are of the kind still popular—the name by a man who wants to let posterity know that he has been in Siheil. Their antiquity endows them with a corporate importance in historical terms out of all proportion to their individual content. Together they provide an account of the comings and goings at the southern boundary of Egypt for hundreds of years. These inscriptions and scenes are not conventionally carved, but were registered on the rocks by a bruising technique. A suitable surface was chosen and the text hammered on the granite with a harder stone pounder,

The boulder on Siheil Island bearing the Famine Inscription.

made probably of dolerite. The hammered area showed up lighter than the surrounding, untouched granite. It was a laborious and not very precise method of recording a text, but the years have not obliterated what was hammered.

One of the strangest and longest of these inscriptions is in the form of a royal proclamation. It purports to commemorate something that happened during the reign of Zoser, who ruled Egypt about 2650 B.C. Egypt made great strides forward in his reign, through the agency of his principal official, Imhotep, an administrator and architect. More than two thousand years later, during the Ptolemaic period, Imhotep's fame became so great that he was honored as a god. He was thought of as the epitome of wisdom, the father of medicine, and was shown as a learned scribe seated on a throne holding an open papyrus scroll on his lap. The Siheil inscription was set up by a king, possibly Ptolemy V, Epiphanes (about 200 B.C.) who may have needed to obtain local prestige in the cataract area. He chose to do it by way of an historical parable. The tale may contain echoes of local traditions concerning the far-off times when Zoser reigned, but for the most part it probably belongs to the genre of historical fictions that are written for the ulterior motives of some later personage.

The Seven-Year Famine

In the eighteenth year of my reign, I, King Zoser, wish to inform the world of the sad state in which Egypt recently found itself. I was in the depths of despair because there had been no flooding by the Nile for seven years. There was scarcely any grain left, nobody had much to eat, and there was no revenue coming in. People could scarcely walk, children cried, old people sat miserably on the ground with their knees bent up. Even the courtiers were in need, while the temples were shut up. Everybody was miserable. In an effort to find out what I could do, I questioned the chief lector-priest of Imhotep. 'In what place does the Nile rise? What god dwells there, that I may enlist his help?'

'I shall go at once to Hermopolis,' answered the priest, 'to do a little research in the library in the temple there, to discover what advice can be culled from the sacred writings.'

In next to no time the priest had returned with the results of his research. 'There is a town in the middle of the Nile,' he said, 'called Elephantine. It is at the very beginning of things; it is the seat from which Re dispatches life to everyone. It is the source of life, the place from which the fertilizing Nile in its flood leaps forth to impregnate the land. The god of that place is Khnum. He allots the lands of Egypt to each god and controls the grain and the birds and the fish and everything on which they live. A survey cord is kept there, and a scribe's palette, ready for the making of assessments of crops. On the east side of the city are great mountains that contain all kinds of precious minerals and hardstones. There are splendid quarries where quarrymen obtain the fine materials used in all the temples of Upper and Lower Egypt, for the stables of sacred animals, for royal tombs, and for all the statues erected in temples and sanctuaries. The products of the mountains are brought to Khnum together with all the plants and flowers that grow in the neighborhood. And in the middle of the river is a wonderful place of relaxation that is covered when the Nile is in flood.'

The priest then instructed me in what could be found in this delectable place and in its neighborhood. He first listed in order of importance the gods and goddesses who were worshiped in the great temple of Khnum on the island of Elephantine, both those deities who lived there by right and those who came on visits and were welcome there. He then enumerated in detail all the kinds of stone obtainable in the mountains round about—stones for building, stones for statues, and precious stones used in the jeweler's art. He also named the rare metals that were mined in the same mountains. He told me many more things about Elephantine until I had a very full idea of its riches. When he had finished, I was full of joy to know that such a place existed in my realm. I ordered the sacred books to be unrolled, I made purifications, organized processions, and made full offerings of all kinds of food and drink to the gods and goddesses of Elephantine whose names had been mentioned.

Some time later, while I lay sleeping peacefully, I dreamed

that the great god Khnum stood before me. At once I did all I could to render him favorable, giving him adoration and making my petition before him, and he answered me in a very friendly way: 'I am Khnum, your maker; with my arms I protect you and help you. I make available for you endless supplies of precious minerals, such as no one else has ever known. Yet there is no work going on. You should be building temples, restoring those buildings that have fallen into ruin, rehabilitating the statues. For I am the great creator-lord who orders everything; I am Nun who has existed from the earliest times; I am the Nile in flood who runs at will; I actuate men and guide them to their moments of destiny. My sanctuary has two gates from which I can let out the water for the flood. It is the flood that brings life to everyone; everything it irrigates continues to live. I shall make the flood rise for you again, and there will be no more years without inundation. The flowers will flourish, and every plant will prosper a million-fold. Want will cease, and all granaries will be filled. The people of Egypt will be happier than ever before.'

When I awoke from my sleep, my mind was full of the

dream; all its details were fixed clearly in my consciousness. With joy in my heart and a sure knowledge that the outcome would be good for my unhappy land, I called my chief scribe and dictated a decree in honor of my father Khnum. It embodied all the provisions he had specified in my dream. They ran as follows:

In the first place, in return for all the god had done for me, I offered him a large tract of land on both sides of the river, stretching from Elephantine southward to Tacompso.

All those who cultivate fields within this territory, both on the river banks and in newly reclaimed areas, should gather their harvests into Khnum's granaries.

Furthermore, all men engaged in catching fish, hunting large and small animals, snaring birds, and all lion-hunters, shall be taxed one-tenth of all that they take by their efforts, and the revenue given to Khnum. All young that are born to domesticated animals in the specified territory are likewise to be handed over.

In addition, all beasts marked for sacrifice, and all other offerings should be given to Khnum, including all the products that arrive at the frontier from Nubia—gold, ivory, ebony, all kinds of plants and minerals and woods—and whatever may be collected as arrears of taxes from the Nubians. There must be no interference on the part of officials who may attempt to divert what should go by right to the Temple of Khnum.

Finally, the whole of this territory, including all the rocky parts and the good cultivable land should belong to Khnum. Officials should be appointed to dwell there and supervise the work of all workers in precious and other metals, and all craftsmen; they should ensure that a tithe of all that is made is remitted to the temple of Khnum. And the same tithe is imposed on the yield of trade and the quarries. Those workmen who are employed in the workshops attached to the Temple of Khnum shall not lack precious metals and other materials they need to make new statues and ritual vessels, and to repair what is damaged. Everything there should be as it was in former times.

Such were the terms of my decree, and I ordered that it be inscribed on a stone set up in a sacred place and also written on a tablet deposited in the god's sanctuary. For it all turned out as I had dreamed. And I also order that the priestly and other officials should make my name live eternally in the Temple of Khnum, Lord of Elephantine.

TALES OF PAST GLORIES

In ancient Egypt it was usual to tell stories about the great personalities of earlier times. In this way, even the most fantastic tales were invested with a familiar background that made them seem more real to the listener. The famous people of the past, remembered largely by vague reputation, became larger than life. As memories of them persisted, so their achievements grew, until their powers were inflated and could only be explained in terms of magic. This kind of transformation happened not only to men of action but also to able administrators who by their wisdom brought prosperity and fame to the land of Egypt. The Egyptians produced no philosophers like the Greeks, but they did have homespun moralists who wrote books of wisdom to instruct the young. Such books were always attributed to the wise men of antiquity, to give them greater authority. If a wise man's reputation lasted long enough, he became venerated in a way comparable with that of a Christian saint. He sometimes became a demigod and shrines were set up in his honor. Sometimes these wise men were called 'magicians,' but in the sense that they were 'holders of the ritual book' —that is, priests who excelled in reciting spells and divining the future.

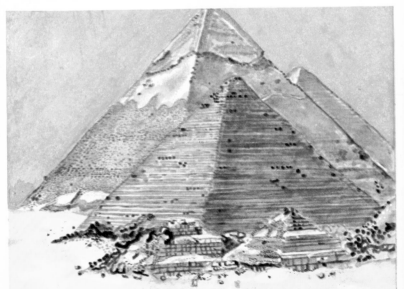

The Pyramids of Giza. The pyramid of Cheops is in the background, and that of Chephren in the center.

The diorite statue of Chephren in the Cairo Museum. About 2550 B.C.

The process of veneration in its early stages can be observed in a group of stories preserved in one papyrus only. It is known as the Westcar Papyrus (after an early owner; it is now in Berlin); it dates from about 1700 B.C., although the stories purport to go back to about 2600 B.C. They are remarkable stories and are presented as if they were being told to the famous King Cheops, the builder of the Great Pyramid. The beginning of the papyrus is lost and with it the part of the narrative setting the scene in which the events took place. It can be inferred that Cheops had arranged a great banquet, and in the course of the entertainment he called upon his sons, in turn, to tell stories about the extraordinary things performed by magicians and wise men in the reigns of the kings who had come before him.

It is not known how many sons Cheops actually had, but only three stories are preserved; the narrators are Chephren, Baufre, and Djedefhor, and only Chephren is a known historical figure. To better understand such stories, keep in mind that Egyptian stories often drew upon many sources, including folk tales, distorted history, and deeprooted cultural traditions. Thus, in the third tale, we catch vibrations from Egypt's matriarchal traditions, where property and descent passed through the female line. We cannot know all these elements, but we can be aware that many different ones are incorporated into such stories.

Cheops and the Magicians

Prince Chephren stood up to speak: 'I shall tell Your Majesty a wonder that happened in the reign of your ancestor Nebka, when he went to the Temple of Ptah. He intended to talk to the chief lector-priest Weba-oner.'

Now it happened that Weba-oner's wife had fallen in love with a man from the town and showed her affection by sending him presents of clothes and messages by her maid. Whenever it was convenient, she sent her maid to bring her lover to Weba-oner's house. In the garden of the house there was a pavilion by a lake, and after some days the man from the town said to Weba-oner's wife, 'Let us pass some time in the pavilion by the lake.' So the wife told the lake-steward to prepare the pavilion, and she and her lover spent the day there eating and drinking until sunset. When evening came, the man of the town went down to the lake to purify himself, while the wife's maid went to the lake-steward and told him what her mistress had been doing.

When the next day dawned, the steward made it his first duty to call on his master, Weba-oner, and tell him the whole story as he had heard it from the maid-servant. Weba-oner showed little anger, but he quietly ordered his steward to bring his magic box. It was a marvelously contrived box made of ebony and inlaid with designs executed in electrum, and it contained materials of strange power. When the box had been brought, he took some wax from it and made a model crocodile, seven hand-breaths long. He then recited magical incantations over the completed model and spoke to it: 'Hear me! When that man of the town comes and bathes in my lake, as now he does every day, go into the water and seize him for me.' When the spell was finished, Weba-oner handed the waxen crocodile to his steward, saying, 'Watch for the moment when that man next comes to bathe in my lake; then throw this crocodile into the water after him.' The steward took the model and went about his regular business of the day, waiting for the moment

when he should carry out his master's orders.

Shortly afterward, Weba-oner's wife sent for the steward and instructed him to prepare the pavilion again. This he did, and the wife and her lover made merry there. When evening came, the man went down to the lake, as was his habit, and the steward threw the waxen crocodile into the water after him. At once it became a real crocodile seven cubits long that seized the lover and carried him off.

Meanwhile, Weba-oner spent seven days with King Nebka, while the man of the town was kept in the depths of the lake without breathing. After this time, Nebka went to the temple, and Weba-oner approached him, saying, 'Will Your Majesty come and see a wonder that has happened during your reign?' So His Majesty went with Weba-oner to the lake, and the priest summoned the crocodile by magic, saying, 'Bring the man to me here.' When the crocodile appeared carrying the man, King Nebka said nervously, 'Surely

Piled offerings painted on the coffin of Djehuty-nakhte. About 1850 B.C. Boston Museum.

this crocodile is dangerous.' Weba-oner bent down and took up the crocodile, which became again a waxen model in his hand.

Then Weba-oner told the king what the man had done with his wife, and the king said to the crocodile, 'Take what belongs to you.' And the crocodile slid down into the depths of the lake, and no one knew where he went with the man of the town. Nebka next ordered that Weba-oner's wife be taken to a piece of open ground to the north of the palace. There she was burned and her remains thrown into the Nile.

'That was the wonder that happened in the reign of your ancestor King Nebka,' said Chephren, 'the work of the chief lector-priest Weba-oner.'

Cheops then ordered an offering to be made to King Nebka, consisting of one thousand loaves of bread, one hundred jugs of beer, an ox, and two packets of incense; and that to the priest Weba-oner should be given one cake, one jug of beer, a large joint of meat, and one packet of incense as a reward

A seated scribe with open papyrus on his lap. From Giza. About 2400 B.C.

for his demonstration of wisdom. And it was done just as Cheops commanded.

Then Prince Baufre stood up to speak: 'I shall tell Your Majesty of a wonder that happened in the reign of your father, King Snofru, the achievement of the chief lector-priest Djadja-emankh.'

One day King Snofru was depressed, and he bid his courtiers discover something to cheer him up; but they were quite unsuccessful. Then he ordered, 'Go, and fetch the chief lector-priest and scribe Djadja-emankh.' When he had come, His Majesty explained how the courtiers had failed to find him any diversion. After a moment's thought Djadja-emankh bowed low and said: 'I think I know of something that will refresh Your Majesty. You have in the grounds of your palace a fine lake on which you sail from time to time. Go boating now, but do not let them man your craft with its usual crew. Order your steward to recruit a crew made up of the prettiest girls to be found in the palace. Let them row your boat. You will find that your spirits will rise as you watch them pulling on the oars. You can sit there, looking at the beautiful thickets around the lake, the pools and the inlets and the verdant banks gliding past, and your heart will be much refreshed.'

The idea pleased King Snofru. 'I shall make arrangements to go at once,' he said. 'Have twenty fine ebony oars brought, decorated with gold and worked with electrum; and twenty girls, fair of form, with well-rounded breasts and plaited hair who should not yet have borne children. And bring twenty net garments which are to be given to the girls to wear after they have taken off their own clothes.' And everything he commanded was done.

When the boat and its unusual crew were ready, Snofru went on board and seated himself comfortably. A wide awning above his head protected him from the rays of the sun, and by his side stood a jar of fine wine and a basket of fruit. Over all the boat was decked with garlands of flowers, and it made a pretty sight as it floated on the lake. But prettier still were the rowers. With friendly banter the two sides called to each other; with even rhythm they sent the boat along, urged on by their leaders. Up and down the lake went the boat and His Majesty was delighted; it made his heart glad to see them row. For a time all went well and then, quite unexpectedly, one of the strokes seated in the stern of the boat got her hair caught in her oar, and a trinket of new turquoise fell from her head into the water. At once she stopped rowing, and all the girls on her side of the boat stopped also. 'You are not rowing?' enquired His Majesty, and they answered, 'Our stroke has stopped rowing.' Snofru said, 'Why aren't you rowing?' 'Because a hair-trinket of new turquoise has fallen from my head into the water,' she said. So His Majesty replied, 'Look here, I will give you another one just the same.' And the girl said, 'I'd rather have my own trinket than a copy.'

Feeling defeated and depressed again, Snofru sent for Djadja-emankh and explained to him what had happened. 'My dear brother, Djadja-emankh, I did precisely what you suggested, and I was much pleased watching the girls row up and down. But then, unfortunately, a hair-trinket of new turquoise belonging to one of the strokes fell into the water, and she stopped rowing. When I urged her to row on, promising to replace the trinket, she said she would rather have her own trinket than a copy. The trip is quite spoiled, and my somber mood has returned. What can you do to help?'

When Djadja-emankh had heard this sorry tale he muttered a magical incantation over the waters of the lake, as the result of which he was able to lift up one half of the water and fold it over on top of the other half. The bottom of one side of the lake was thus revealed, and there, lying on a piece of pottery, was the hair-trinket of new turquoise. Djadja-emankh then went down into the depth of the lake where the water had been, and he retrieved the hair-trinket and brought it back, handing it to its owner. It was a remarkable feat, for the water of the lake had originally been eighteen feet deep in the middle; when folded back, it measured thirty-six feet. Now that the trinket had been recovered, the priest muttered another incantation, and the water unfolded itself and went back to its former position. King Snofru was much relieved by this happy outcome, for the girl was satisfied and prepared to row again. So they set off once more, and His Majesty spent the whole day making merry and having a good time. When the day was over, the king rewarded Djadja-emankh with all kinds of presents in return for the great feat that he had performed.

'That then was the wonderful thing that happened during the reign of your noble predecessor, King Snofru,' said the prince Baufre to Cheops. 'It was the work of the chief lector-priest and scribe Djadja-emankh.'

When Baufre had finished speaking, His Majesty King Cheops ordered that a substantial offering be made to the memory of his famous predecessor, Snofru, consisting of one thousand loaves of bread, one hundred jugs of beer, a whole ox, and two packets of incense. For Djadja-emankh, the king ordered one cake, one jug of beer, one large joint of meat, and one packet of incense as a reward for his demonstration of wisdom. And it was done just as Cheops had commanded.

Then Prince Djedefhor stood up to speak: 'So far, Your Majesty, you have only heard stories about marvels performed

by wise men of earlier times. It is impossible to prove whether these tales are true or false. But what about the deeds of a man of your own time, whom you do not know?' 'What deeds are they, my son?' asked Cheops.

'There is a man called Dedi,' said Djedefhor. 'He lives in Djed-snofru and is one hundred and ten years old. He has an enormous appetite and knows many marvelous things; he can rejoin a severed head to its body, make a lion walk behind him, and he knows the number of the secret rooms of the Temple of Thoth.' Now Cheops had always wanted to know the number of these rooms to reproduce them in his tomb; so he sent Djedefhor to fetch Dedi.

As soon as the traveling boats were made ready, Djedefhor set out from the royal residence and journeyed south to Djed-snofru. When they reached the town, the boats were made fast at the quay and Djedefhor enquired where Dedi lived. The men who had helped to moor the boats told him that Dedi's house lay some distance from the river. It would not have done for the prince to walk so far, and a litter was brought

from the baggage boat. It was of fine workmanship and richly decorated; the frame was of ebony and the carrying poles of some other wood covered with gold foil. Reclining on soft cushions, Djedefhor took his ease as he traveled in the litter over the rough tracks which led through the fields. After a little time the prince's party reached Dedi's house, and the litter was set down in front of the door where Dedi could be seen lying on a mat. Two slaves attended him, one massaging his head and the other rubbing his feet.

Djedefhor descended from his litter and, approaching the old man, greeted him and said: 'Your condition is like living before old age,' by which he meant to compliment Dedi on his fine appearance. He then explained the purpose of his visit. 'I have come to fetch you for King Cheops. You will enjoy the fine fare the king will provide, and he will arrange a splendid burial for you when your time comes.' Dedi greeted him in the manner due to a king's son and agreed to return with Djedefhor. Together they went down to the river, and Dedi asked for a special boat to be made available for his children and

his books. Two extra vessels were provided, and they set off, Dedi traveling in the same boat as Djedefhor.

After they reached the palace, the prince reported to Cheops, and the king ordered Dedi to be brought to him in the great hall. 'How comes it that I have never seen you, Dedi?' said the king. 'Only he who is summoned comes,' replied Dedi. 'Behold! I have been summoned, and now I come.'

'Is it true that you can join a severed head to its body?' asked His Majesty.

'Indeed I can, my Lord,' said Dedi.

'Splendid!' said the king. 'Bring here a newly executed prisoner.'

But Dedi objected, 'It is forbidden to do such a thing to one of the noble race of men.'

So a goose was brought, and its body placed on one side of the hall and its head on the other. Dedi muttered a spell and the two parts moved toward each other and were reunited;

the goose stood up cackling. He then did the same with another goose and with an ox, and he tamed a lion with magic.

After these remarkable demonstrations Cheops knew that what he had been told of Dedi's powers was true. Now he could ask him the question for which he badly needed the answer. So he called Dedi and said: 'Is it indeed true, as I have heard, that you know the number of the secret rooms of the temple of Thoth?' 'If it please Your Majesty,' answered Dedi, 'I do not know the number, but I do know where it can be found.' 'Where?' asked Cheops. 'In a flint box in a room in the Temple of Heliopolis.' 'Bring it to me,' said the king. 'Alas, no!' said Dedi. 'I cannot bring it; it must be brought by the eldest of three children in the womb of Red-djedet.' 'Who is this woman?' demanded the king. 'She is the wife of Ra-user, a priest of Re, Lord of Sakhebu, who has conceived these children by Re himself. He told her that in time they would be kings in this land.' When he heard this, Cheops became sad, but Dedi comforted him. 'Don't worry, Your Majesty, for your son and his son will rule before the first of Red-djedet's children.' Cheops then asked him when they could expect Red-djedet to give birth. 'On the fifteenth day of the first month of winter,' answered Dedi. 'That is a bad time for traveling,' said Cheops. 'The water will be low and I doubt if my boat could negotiate the sandbanks to reach Sakhebu. Yet I should like to visit the temple of Re there at that time.' 'Pray do not worry, Your Majesty,' said Dedi in his turn. 'I shall make sure that there are at least six feet of water covering the sand banks then, so your boat should pass to Sakhebu without difficulty.' Much relieved, Cheops retired to his quarters, commanding that Dedi be installed in Djedefhor's house with massive quantities of food and drink for his use. And it was done as Cheops commanded.

The story then continues with the birth of the divine children.

About this time it happened that Red-djedet began to suffer her pains, and Re of Sakhebu said to Isis, Nephthys, Meskhent, Heqet, and Khnum, 'Go, and help deliver the three children in Red-djedet's womb—those who will be kings in this land. For they are the ones who will build your temples and provide your offerings.' The four goddesses disguised themselves as dancing-girls and departed with Khnum in attendance. When they reached the house they found Red-djedet's husband Ra-user in a state of distraction, and they at once offered to help Red-djedet in her labors. Ra-user led them to his wife's chamber and left them with her. They closed the door and placed themselves around Red-djedet. One by one the children were born, each being eighteen inches long and equipped with marks of divine royalty. As each appeared, Isis greeted him with a welcome that included a clever reference to his future name as king of Egypt. The first was Userkaf; the second, Sahure; and the third, Kakai. When each was washed, the goddess, Meskhent declared his kingship and Khnum conferred health on his body. Finally the deities went to Ra-user and told him of the birth of sons to his wife. In gratitude he gave them barley before they departed.

When they returned home, Isis said to her companions: 'How could we have gone to her and yet worked no marvel that we could report to Re, the children's real father?' So they made three crowns and hid them in the barley and under cover of a storm returned to Ra-user's house, begging to leave the barley in a locked chamber until they could come again.

After Red-djedet had completed two weeks' purification, she began to organize a party, but found that the only barley available for making beer was that kept locked up for the dancing-girls. She instructed her servant to borrow some, but when the girl went to the chamber she heard the sound of great jollity coming forth. She told Red-djedet, who traced the sounds to the barley-sack, which she took and made safe in a chest. When Ra-user came home, she told him and he was delighted. Together they sat down and celebrated.

A few days later, after receiving a beating for behaving badly, Red-djedet's maid announced that she knew that her mistress had borne three kings, and she declared that she would tell King Cheops. Her brother, however, horrified at her threat to betray Red-djedet, beat her, too; and when she went to fetch water, a crocodile seized her. At once, the brother went to tell Red-djedet, who was in despair at the thought that she would be denounced to Cheops.

(Here, unfortunately, the papyrus breaks off, and we do not know what happened to Red-djedet, the priest's wife. But we do know that her sons survived and were, in time, to be the first three kings of the 5th Dynasty.)

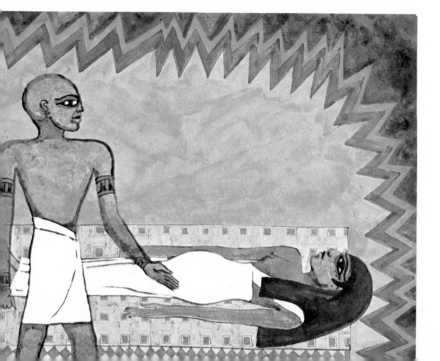

THE CLASSIC TRAVELER'S YARN

This tale, a classic of its period and one of the most often reprinted ancient Egyptian tales in our own day, exists in only one papyrus. This is preserved in the Hermitage in Leningrad; it was only discovered about 1880, and it is not known exactly where it came from. Scholars, however, have been able to date the papyrus at about 2000 B.C. The background circumstances of the story itself are also uncertain because the papyrus that contains the text is damaged at the beginning. But from the opening of the preserved portion it emerges that a certain high official, usually described in translation as a Count, is very anxious about the kind of reception he is going to receive when he returns to court and presents his report on what may have been a difficult and possibly abortive expedition to Nubia. At the time when the action may be assumed to have occurred, Egyptian power was not well established in the lands to the south of the First Cataract. From a very early period the attractions of trade had led adventurous Egyptians into what they

called the Land of Kush. They sought the exotic products of tropical Africa that they could obtain by barter in the northern Sudan. It is unlikely that Egyptian traders ever penetrated to equatorial regions from which the desirable goods came. Kush also yielded gold, and it was undoubtedly the search for a safe source of this metal that eventually led the Egyptians to establish themselves firmly in Nubia. The earlier expeditions were probably quite small and their success depended on the kind of reception, good or ill, they met at the hands of the native tribes of Nubia. Sometimes things went wrong and then the expedition returned empty-handed. This kind of failure may form the background of this story.

The Count is dejected and fears that he may fall out of favor with the king because of his lack of success. His companion tries to comfort him by telling him of another unfortunate expedition in which he took part, the outcome of which was unexpectedly favorable. They talk just after their arrival on the southern border of Egypt. The companion speaks.

The Tale of the Shipwrecked Sailor

All's well, Count, we are home again. The boats have come to land and are properly secured. The men are giving praise to God and embrace each other. For we are all here safely; none of our party has been lost. We have come back in peace to our own country. Now pay close attention to what I have to say, for you know that I am not much given to unnecessary speaking. When the time comes for you to face the king, wash yourself properly and meet his questions with confidence. Do not hesitate when you speak, because the way in which you speak will determine your fair treatment. Nevertheless, you do as you think fit, for you will get bored with my chatter.

Yet let me tell you about a similar thing that happened to me once when I went to the mines for the king. As you know, the only way to reach the barren lands where the mines are is by ship. Every care had been taken to fit out our expedition with all we should need for the journey and for our work.

We had a fine boat specially built, made of the choicest timbers of Syria. It was bigger than any boat of its kind; no similar expedition has been so favored by His Majesty in this respect. It was 180 feet in length and 60 feet wide; it stood high in the water and had roomy cabins and dry holds for the equipment. We also had a hand-picked company of craftsmen and laborers, while the crew was the best in Egypt. The company on board numbered 120 in all, and when we left harbor we were full of confidence.

A sea voyage is always disagreeable, but on this occasion nobody was afraid, because the captain and the crew were so experienced. Nothing bothered them, and they could predict a storm long before it arrived. Now a great tempest broke out on this voyage while we were still at sea, and it hit us before we could make land. The wind roared and the sea rose with waves 12 feet high. In the end, the ship broke up and everyone on board perished except myself. A great wave carried me and cast me on the shore of an island, and there I lay for three days all by myself, hiding in the cover provided by a tree.

When I emerged from my shelter, driven out by hunger, I was surprised to find the island a positive paradise. There were figs and dates, all kinds of vegetables, including cucumbers as big as if they had been cultivated. There was fish in the water and fowl in the bush, and I had a splendid time eating all I wanted. When I was satisfied, I made a fire so that I could offer up a burnt sacrifice to God; in a distant land, away from Egypt, only by the smoke of a burnt offering can you reach God.

At that moment I heard a terrible noise that seemed to be a great wave from the sea. The earth shook, and the trees around me were split like matchwood. When I opened my eyes, I saw a huge snake advancing on me. He was 45 feet long with a beard more than three feet long. His body was overlaid with gold, and his eyebrows were inlaid with real lapis-lazuli. It was clear that he was very clever. As I lay prostrate on the ground before him, he spoke: 'Tell me, little fellow, what brings you to this island? Tell me at once or I shall shrivel you to a cinder.' He went on talking, but I heard only a little of what he said because I fainted away. Apparently he then picked me up in his mouth and took me to his lair where he laid me down unharmed. As soon as I came around, he again asked me, 'Tell me, little fellow, what brings you to this island in the sea?'

So I told him the story of how I had gone on a royal mission to the mines and how the boat had been manned with the best crew available; how a tempest had overtaken us and destroyed the boat, and how I alone had survived, being cast up by a wave onto his island. He sensed my fear and comforted me: 'Do not be afraid, little fellow. God has saved you to bring you here to please me. This island is a marvelous place; it has everything. So enjoy it for a time. After four months a boat will come with a crew containing men whom you know. They will take you back to the royal city, and you will in the end die in your own town.' He then went on to tell me a sad story of his own, one which was not unlike my experience.

'How happy,' said he, 'is one who can tell of what he has suffered when it all lies in the past! Years ago I lived on this island with my relations, and there were young ones among us. In all we numbered 75 snakes, including my relations and the children; and there was also a young girl. One day, when I was not with the rest, a star fell and its fire destroyed them all. I found them lying together, a tangled mass of corpses, and at that sight I too could have died for them. That is what happened to me. But for you the outlook is brighter. If you are patient, you will hug your children soon, and kiss your wife, and see your home—all the best things you could want.'

Again I prostrated myself before him, and said: 'I shall tell my lord, the king, all about your might and describe your greatness. I shall send you oils and fragrant perfumes and incense such as is used to propitiate all the gods. Your tale I shall tell everywhere, and I shall arrange for a special vote of thanks to be returned to you by the supreme council. Beyond all that, I shall make burnt sacrifices for you and send you ships weighed down with the best things of Egypt. I shall do just what should be done for a god who loves men in a distant land which is unknown to men.'

He laughed at what I said, as if it were a vain boast. 'You have not got much incense. I am the ruler of Punt, and incense is my monopoly. And that special oil you would send me is the particular product of this island. When you go from here, you will never again see this island, for it will disappear into the waves.'

In due course the ship came, as he had promised, and when I climbed a tall tree to see it arrive, I could recognize some of the men on board. I ran to tell of its arrival and found that the snake already knew. 'Farewell, my little fellow,' he said. 'Go to your home and your children. All I ask is that you speak well of me in your town.'

I prostrated myself before him and he presented me with a huge load of oils and incense, malachite, giraffe's tails, tusks of ivory, hounds, monkeys, apes, and all the products of the island. We said our goodbyes and I went down to the boat, calling together the soldiers to join me there in praising the lord of the island. As we left the island I could not tell what feeling was strongest in my breast. I was glad to be rescued and I longed to be back in my city, to see my wife and children. Yet a voyage of many days lay ahead, and I no longer had any confidence in boats that go to sea. What is more, I could only fear the reception I would receive when the king learned about the failure of our expedition. In the same moment I was glad and fearful and full of foreboding. And yet I need not have feared. After a voyage of two months we reached the royal city and I made my report to the king, presenting him with the gifts I had brought. He was delighted and thanked me before the supreme council. He made me a Companion and gave me two hundred servants.

'Now just consider what happened to me when I returned home after a bad experience. It is good to hear what others have to say.'

But the Count replied: 'Do not be so smug, my friend. Do you usually give water to a bird that will be killed in the morning?'

THE TALE OF A RICH KING

One of the greatest of Egyptian kings was Ramesses II who reigned for over sixty years during the thirteenth century B.C. He was a great fighter and a great builder, but his reputation as a builder rests on firmer ground than his reputation as a fighter. The ruins of vast buildings bearing his name can be found throughout Egypt, so that the visitor is constantly reminded of him. And this is just what Ramesses wanted. He was a notable propagandist in his own cause, and in the course of his long reign he succeeded in placing the stamp of his name on almost every important building in Egypt in addition to those he had built himself. In this way he 'made his name live', as the ancient Egyptians would have said; and indeed it lived on in popular memory for many centuries. When the Greek traveler and historian Herodotus visited Egypt about 450 B.C., the memories of Ramesses had become blurred, but there

Ramesses II as a young man. About 1290 B.C. Turin Museum.

can be little doubt that he was the king about whom several stories were told to the interested Greek. (Apropos of which, we might keep in mind that although Herodotus is called 'the father of history,' he is also known as 'the father of lies'—in reference to the fact that he seems to have passed on just about any wild tale anyone told him.) The following tale about Rhampsinitus, as the king was called in Herodotus' version, is wholly unhistorical in its contents. And there are undoubtedly elements in the story similar to those in other nations' folklore. But even if every detail in the story is not originally Egyptian, the work as a whole seems typically Egyptian in character, being very much like the romances preserved in Egyptian papyri of the period—that is, about 450 B.C. (One of these, concerning Khaemwese, the son of Ramesses II, we shall be reading shortly.)

The view into the 'treasure house' of Tutankhamon's tomb at the time of discovery.

The Treasure of Rhampsinitus

The story goes that Rhampsinitus was exceptionally rich. So great were his treasures that none of the kings who had come before him could have competed with him in this respect. In the many years of his reign he had won mighty victories, and his armies had brought back much booty to Egypt. He always chose the finest trophies for his own collection and never allowed a distribution of the loot before he had personally inspected it. Subject kings and allied rulers soon learned how best they could win favor in his eyes. On every proper occasion they sent him the richest vessels, the most elaborate chests, the most precious jewels. Everything of special beauty or great value was placed in the royal collection and carefully listed by the king's secretary. His treasure was a matter of great pride to the king, but it was also a source of much worry. He knew men's greed, and he feared that someone would plot to steal what he could. So Rhampsinitus

Silver jug with gold antelope handle from a treasure found at Bubastis. About 1250 B.C. Cairo Museum.

decided to have a special treasury constructed to hold it all. The building was solid and without entrance from outside the royal palace; it could only be approached from the king's own suite of rooms. The architect of the treasury, however, was a crafty man who saw an opportunity to do himself some good. In his design he included a secret entrance marked by a cunningly fitted block of stone that could be removed by two men with ease and by one man with a little difficulty. He made no use of this secret entrance immediately after the king had stored his valuables in his new strong-room, but he planned to use it in due course as need demanded. After some time, however, the architect fell ill, and he felt himself close to death; so he called his two sons to his bedside and told them his great secret. He explained how he had from the first intended to use the secret entrance for their advantage, and he provided them with all the necessary details whereby they could identify the loose block of stone. In this way, he promised them, they could control the king's treasure.

No sooner had the architect died than his sons set about profiting from the information. At the first opportunity, they went by night to the palace, found the treasury,

identified the secret entrance, moved the block of stone, and climbed into the chamber. By the light of a taper they moved among the great storage jars that filled the room, dumbfounded by the wonderful things they saw. The young men were no fools and realized that they could only exploit this 'mine' if they were careful. They agreed that they should never take more than one or two pieces at a time, and then only things that could easily be disposed of. At first all went well, and their thefts were judicious and minor. But as time went on they became bolder and took larger and finer things. So when Rhampsinitus next came to inspect the royal treasury he was amazed to discover that several notable pieces were missing from his hoard. He was quite at a loss to see how they could have been taken, for all the seals on the one entrance door had been intact before he had entered. After several further inspections, when again he found much treasure missing, he realized that someone was systematically robbing him and that something had to be done to stop the thefts.

So Rhampsinitus arranged for some crafty traps to be set near the jars which contained his treasure, and again he sealed the entrance door and waited. Shortly after this the two sons came again to the palace, removed the secret stone, and entered the chamber. The first to enter went straight to the jars and immediately became trapped in one of the snares. He realized that there was nothing they could do to release him, and in desperation prevailed on his brother to cut off his head and abandon him to his fate. At least in this way their identity would be kept secret. The brother saw the sense in this suggestion at once, cut off the head, and withdrew from the chamber.

The next day when the king came to the chamber to inspect the traps, he was astonished to find the headless body of the thief, but still no sign of a door through which he could have entered. He therefore ordered the corpse to be hung up outside the town walls, and instructed guards to sit in wait until they observed anyone weeping at the sight.

When the mother of the thiefs heard about the exposure of the body, she wept greatly, and prevailed on her other son to devise a way of retrieving the corpse. Otherwise she threatened to go to the king and tell him the whole story.

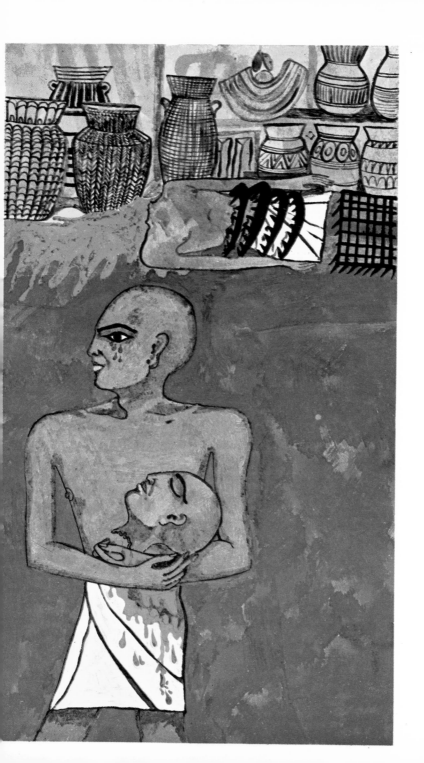

The son tried to dissuade her but in the end agreed to go.

He took some donkeys, loaded them with skins of wine, and drove them to the place where the body hung. As the donkeys passed the guards, he loosened the necks of some of the skins and the wine poured out. In feigned anguish he cried out, and the guards ran forward eagerly with pots to catch what wine they could. At once the thief turned on the guards in fury, and they in turn did their best to calm him down. After a time he pretended to regain his good humor, and he drove his donkeys off the road to adjust their loads. By now he had become quite friendly with the guards and he gave them one of the wine skins. The unusual incident had relaxed their vigilance to such an extent that the guards settled down to the wine and were joined in their party by the thief. Before long all the guards had drunk too much, and one by one they fell asleep where they sat. The theif, however, had only pretended to match them in their drinking and was quite sober. As soon as he was sure that none of the guards would trouble him he set about recovering his brother's body from its shameful position. At length he succeeded, and loaded the headless corpse on one of the donkeys, covering it up with some of the empty wine skins. Just before he left with his sad load, he took a last look at the guards and was struck by the foolishness of their situation. He was by nature something of a joker and could not resist a final insult to remind them of their folly. Taking a razor from the belongings of one of the guards he shaved off the right sides of all their beards. He then took the body home to his mother.

When they brought the news of the theft of the body to Rhampsinitus the next day, he was furious at having been outwitted again. Determined to get the better of his tormentor, he devised a plan whereby the thief might be tricked into revealing himself by trying his luck too far. His plan was such that it can hardly be believed. He called his daughter and proposed that she should go into the town and establish herself as a harlot in a brothel. She should then let it be known that she would entertain any client who presented himself. But he instructed her first to put a question to her visitors before she allowed them to enjoy what she had to offer. She should ask each one to tell her what was the

craftiest and most wicked thing that he had ever done. If anyone claimed to have robbed the royal treasury and stolen the thief's body, she should seize hold of him and not allow him to escape.

When she had settled herself in a suitable establishment, the thief soon heard of her and learned that she always asked the same question before she granted her favors. He realized at once what the king had plotted and he decided to try and outwit his royal adversary once again. Before he went, he managed to get hold of the body of a man who had just died, and he cut off one of the arms at the shoulder. This he arranged under his cloak; and so equipped he set out for the royal harlot's house. No sooner had he been ushered into her chamber than she asked him the question which she put to all her clients: 'Tell me what is the craftiest and most wicked deed that you have ever committed?' The thief answered: 'I think that the wickedest thing I ever did was to cut off the head of my brother when he was caught in the king's treasury where we had gone to steal. But the cleverest thing I ever did came after, when the king had the headless body hung up by the town walls, and I managed to steal it from the guards by making them drunk.' As soon as

the princess heard him make this confession in his boastful way, she realized that her quest was over, and she threw herself on the thief to catch him. In the darkness he turned so that she seized his extra arm, and taking advantage of the confusion he slipped away, leaving the severed arm in her hand.

When the princess returned to the palace and told her father, he felt he could no longer go on hounding this remarkable thief. Such a man was too talented to be punished for simple theft and trickery. Rhampsinitus therefore sent out messengers and heralds to advertise that a free pardon awaited the thief and that he would receive a fine reward if he revealed who he was. When he heard this proclamation, the thief saw that he had triumphed, and he trusted the word of the king that he would not be harmed. So he went boldly to the palace and entered the royal presence.

Rhampsinitus was delighted to meet his old enemy and greeted him with real pleasure. He admitted that he thought that the thief was the cleverest of men, rewarded him with much treasure, and gave him his daughter as wife.

'The Egyptians,' Rhampsinitus declared, 'beat the rest of the world in wisdom, and this man beats all other Egyptians.'

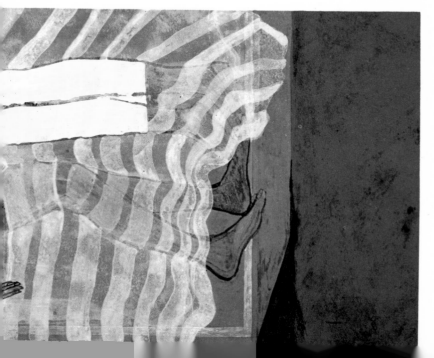

HISTORY AS PROPAGANDA

About 1270 B.C. a marriage took place between Ramesses II, the great Egyptian king, and a daughter of the Hittite king. For a great many years the Hittites, whose empire lay in northern Syria and in Anatolia, had offered the most serious threat to the security of the lands over which Egypt held sway in western Asia. The growth of Hittite power continued, and finally Ramesses was obliged to take the field himself. A great battle was fought at Qadesh in Syria, the outcome of which was indecisive. Both sides claimed the victory, while Ramesses built up for himself a remarkable reputation for personal bravery based on his supposed crucial role in the battle. The truth seems to have been less dramatic. Neither side felt able to renew the struggle, and a formal peace treaty was drawn up between Ramesses and Khattusilis, the Hittite king. The peace was further strengthened by marriage. Much diplomatic activity and a great deal of letter-writing preceded the settle-

The stele in the Louvre Museum containing the tale of the Princess of Bakhtan. About 200 B.C.

ment of the match, and Ramesses was so pleased with the successful outcome of his efforts that he placed a great inscription commemorating the event in several temples. The princess, who was given the Egyptian name Mahorneferure, or Maneferure, was welcomed on her arrival with much ceremony, and it is clear that the marriage was regarded as of the greatest importance both at the time and in subsequent ages. To such an extent did the memory of the event persist that it was used in a garbled form in a text set up in Ptolemaic times to honor the god Khons. This god was one of the principal Theban deities, and in the Late Period he was worshiped in several forms in special temples within the great complex of the Temple of Amon at Karnak. It is this garbled version (preserved on an engraved stele, or stone slab, dating from about 200 B.C.) that we know today. And as will be quite clear, this version is a deliberate historical fiction—like 'The Seven-Year Famine' we have already read—written as a form of official propaganda to justify contemporary acts by the authorities at the temple at Karnak. We must read it, then, in that spirit, keeping aware of the germ of history, but being wary of the flower of propaganda.

The Princess of Bakhtan

Ramesses was in Syria on one of his annual visits of inspection when the time came for the various chiefs and princes to bring him their tribute of gold and silver, lapis-lazuli and turquoise, and precious woods. Among the tributary chiefs was the Prince of Bakhtan, a land so distant that it has never been identified. This prince was determined to impress the great Pharaoh; he brought with him exceptional fine gifts —wonderfully wrought vessels, rare spices and perfumes, spirited horses, and fast chariots. In addition to all these treasures, he brought what he prized above all else in his realm, his eldest daughter. She had all the virtues and all the graces; she was intelligent and understanding; she was the best he could offer to Ramesses. The Egyptian king was delighted with this unusual gift and fell deeply in love with the girl. He gave her the Egyptian name Neferure and invested her with the honors of a royal wife when they returned to Egypt.

Now it happened that in the twenty-third year of his reign, Ramesses was in Thebes taking part in the cermonies and celebrations connected with the great Opet Festival, when he was told that a messenger had arrived from the Prince of Bakhtan, bringing many presents for the royal wife. When the messenger was brought into the audience-chamber, he prostrated himself before Ramesses, saying: 'I have come to you, sovereign lord of my master, on business concerned with Bentresh, the younger sister of your wife Neferure. A sickness pervades her body. Can your majesty send a specialist to see her?'

It so happened that Egyptian doctors were at that time famed throughout the world as masters of diagnosis, brilliant in treatment, and more skilled in effecting cures than the physicians of any other nation. They understood the workings of the body and divined the secrets of the mind; they were craftsmen and magicians at the same time. So when the messenger presented his master's request to Ramesses, the great king summoned his advisers and officials together. First he ordered them to listen to what the messenger had to say, and then he commanded: 'Go through the lists of our most skilled

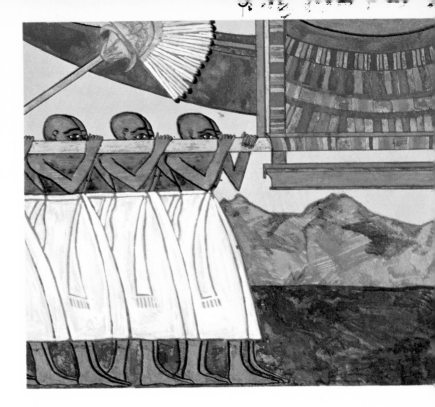

doctors, and bring me the one who would best be able to treat this case.' After considering the matter in committee, the advisers recommended the royal scribe Djehuty-em-heb, who presented himself before the king. Without delay, Ramesses instructed him to accompany the messenger to Bakhtan.

As soon as possible after he had reached Bakhtan, Djehuty-em-heb made an examination of Bentresh and diagnosed that she was possessed by a spirit of such power that he himself was powerless to tackle it. So he told the Prince of Bakhtan, and he sent again to Ramesses to ask him to dispatch a god to help exorcise the spirit. His messenger arrived at Thebes in the first month of summer in the twenty-sixth year of Ramesses' reign, while the Amun Festival was in progress.

When Ramesses had heard the message from the Prince of Bakhtan, he went to the temple of the god called Khons Neferhotep and said to the image of the god: 'I speak to you in the matter of the daughter of the Prince of Bakhtan.' The image was then taken to the shrine of another form of the god who was known as Khons-the-Contriver-in-Thebes, a god parti-

cularly able to drive out evil spirits. 'If you turn to Khons the Contriver,' said Ramesses to Khons Neferhotep, 'he will be sent to Bakhtan.' Khons Neferhotep indicated his willingness by nodding his head twice. 'Reinforce him therefore with your magical essence, and we shall send him to Bakhtan to save the princess,' said Ramesses. Again the god indicated his willingness, and he then passed his magical essence into Khons the Contriver.

As soon as the image of Khons the Contriver was charged with magic, Ramesses ordered it to be carried down to the great sacred boat, and it was sent out on its errand of mercy, accompanied by transport boats and chariots and horses. The journey to Bakhtan took a year and five months, and when the procession reached its goal, the Prince of Bakhtan and his officials came out to welcome the god. Throwing himself on his face before the divine figure, the prince said, 'By the command of the king Ramesses have you come to bestow your grace on us.'

Without delay Kons the Contriver was taken to the chamber

where Bentresh lay. There she was found, still possessed by the spirit, which had failed to yield to the skill of Djehuty-em-heb. The god moved beside the princess and passed his magical essence into her. In a moment she found herself restored to health, while the evil spirit, which had lived so long within her, addressed Khons the Contriver: 'Be welcome, great god, who drives out evil spirits. Bakhtan is now your city, its inhabitants are your slaves, and I too am your slave. Now I shall return to the place from which I came, so as to satisfy your wish in the matter for which you came to this city. May your divine majesty order the celebration of a festival in which I and the Prince of Bakhtan can participate.' The image of Khons the Contriver then made a sign to the priest who attended him, who said, 'Let the Prince of Bakhtan make a great offering to this spirit.'

While Khons the Contriver was closeted with Bentresh and engaged in subduing the evil spirit, the Prince of Bakhtan attended by his high officials and his bodyguard waited close by in an antechamber. The noise that issued from the princess' room as the god came to terms with the spirit was terrifying.

The atmosphere was full of magic, and the tension generated within the room was felt by those who waited without. At length the priest in charge of the divine image came out and conveyed the god's message to the prince. A cry of joy went up and immediately arrangements were made to celebrate a festival. Great offerings were prepared and placed before Khons the Contriver, and the spirit that had occupied the body of the princess of Bakhtan, and everyone else spent a merry day celebrating. When it was all over the spirit departed, obeying the command of Khons the Contriver. And then the Prince of Bakhtan and all the people of Bakhtan gave themselves up to great rejoicing for at last the land was freed from the spirit that had troubled it.

So successful had the god been in achieving what he had been sent to do that the Prince of Bakhtan thought he might try and delay his departure. 'I'll do what I can,' he thought, 'to make the god stay here and not return to Egypt.' So he avoided committing himself in the matter and succeeded in delaying the god for three years and nine months. One day, however, while the prince lay asleep in his bed, he had a vivid dream. In it he saw the god leaving the shrine in which he lived. He

did not come out in the form of his usual image which was that of a man, but he flew out as a falcon made of gold. The prince watched the bird fly up into the heavens and direct its course to Egypt.

At once he woke up in trembling in body and conscious of a great guilt, for he realized that the dream meant that the god wished to go home to Egypt. So he summoned the priest who looked after Khons the Contriver and said to him: 'It seems that your god is still here in Bakhtan with us. It is high time that he went back to Egypt. So get his chariot ready for the return journey.' In this way at last he urged the departure of the god, and with him he sent an enormous number of presents. Every kind of treasure was included in the gift, and he added a substantial detachment of soldiers and a great many horses.

When the moment of departure came, the whole population

The hypostyle hall of the Temple of Khons at Karnak. About 1100 B.C.

Ramesses II presents a collar to the god Khons in a scene from
the temple of the god in Karnak.

of the city of Bakhtan turned out, lining the roads to cheer the
divine image on its way back to Egypt.

The journey home was made without incident, and when
the procession arrived safely in Thebes, the first thing that
Khons the Contriver did was to go directly to the Temple of
Khons Neferhotep. There he approached the resident god who
had inspired him before he left on his errand of mercy, and he
laid before him all the gifts that the Prince of Bakhtan had
given him. For it was the magical essence of Khons Neferhotep
that had driven out the spirit possessing Bentresh. Everything
was deposited there, and when Khons the Contriver returned
to his own temple, he took none of the gifts with him. He
actually reached his own temple safely on the nineteenth day
of the second winter month in the thirty-third year of the reign
of the Pharaoh Ramesses II.

A WISE PRIEST LEARNS A LESSON

Not only was Ramesses II a principal character in tales of the Late Period in Egypt, so also was his Khaemwese. Ramesses in his long life fathered a large family by his many wives —at least 111 sons, according to certain records. None of his sons achieved greater fame during his reign than Khaemwese, who also seems to have been a great favorite of his father. In his earlier years, Khaemwese took part in military expeditions and earned some glory as a soldier. But his reputation in his lifetime and afterward rested especially on his achievements as High Priest of Ptah in Memphis. Ptah, the great artificer of the gods, was a very wise deity, and his priests formed the most intellectual of the priestly colleges in Egypt. Khaemwese, it seems, was never considered the crown prince, and he devoted himself to the exercise of his important priestly office. It was he who organized the great ceremonies that marked the various jubilees celebrated by Ramesses during his long reign.

Statue of Khaemwese. About 1280 B.C. British Museum.

The ruins of the Temple of Ptah in Memphis.

As the master of the secrets of his divine lord Ptah, he was by right a great magician and seer. He died before his father and was buried in the desert cemetery at Saqqara; his tomb, his mummy (now in the Cairo Museum), statues, records, and various objects associated with Khaemwese all testify to the high regard his contemporaries had for him. Moreover, the fame of his wisdom and magic powers persisted, and he became the protagonist of many apocryphal stories. A series of tales concerning Khaemwese is preserved on a papyrus in the Cairo Museum. This actual document was inscribed in about the third century B.C., but its contents are probably of greater age. (The beginning is missing, but there is also a fragment of another version and scholars have been able to piece the story together.) In the story, Khaemwese is shown as someone fascinated by magic, and he undergoes several trials before he learns to leave the supernatural to those who understood it properly. What is also most interesting is to see how the Egyptians could tell a story about such a great personage and yet show him with such human weaknesses.

Khaemwese and Tabubu

When Khaemwese was High Priest of Ptah, he came to know that a remarkable magical book lay in the tomb of a prince called Neferkaptah. He learned where the tomb was in the cemetery of Memphis, and he entered it with his half-brother Anhurerau. There he found the spirits of Neferkaptah, of his wife Ahwere, and of their child Mer-ib. Between Neferkaptah and Ahwere lay a magical book that radiated light like the sun. Khaemwese told the spirits that he had come to collect the book, but they refused to surrender it because they had given their lives for it. As Khaemwese persisted, they told him their sad story, hoping to convince him of the danger that lay in store if he took the book. The High Priest, however, was unwilling to be distracted from his purpose, and eventually Neferkaptah suggested they play checkers for the book. Khaemwese gladly agreed but was beaten game after game; and after each defeat Neferkaptah struck him on the head with the checker board, driving him into the ground like a peg. In desperation, Khaemwese sent Anhurerau to Pharaoh who dispatched a strong amulet to help his son. As soon as the amulet was placed on Khaemwese's head he leapt out of the ground and, taking advantage of the surprise created by his sudden release, he snatched the book and fled from the tomb. The first thing he did was to go to Pharaoh and show him his prize. Ramesses, suspecting that trouble would follow, advised his son to return the book to the tomb, taking with him as magical protection a forked stick in his hand and a lighted brazier on his head. But Khaemwese paid no attention to this advice and kept the book, spending all his time looking at it and reading from it to those who were near him.

Some time later Khaemwese was strolling about the great court of the Temple of Ptah in Memphis when he saw a very beautiful woman. She was unusually striking in appearance, and as she walked about, resplendent with gold ornaments, she was accompanied by two male house-servants and a number of maidservants. As soon as Khaemwese looked at her he did not know where on earth he was, and he ordered his page to find out all he could about her. The boy went up one of the lady's maids and questioned her, and she answered: 'She

is Tabubu, the daughter of the priest of the goddess Bastet, whose shrine is in the suburb of Ankhtawy. She has come here to worship the great god Ptah.'

When the page reported back to Khaemwese, and told him about Tabubu, he said: 'Go now to that maid and tell her that the High Priest Khaemwese, son of Ramesses, sends to ask whether she will spend an hour with him for ten pieces of gold; or if there is any accusation against her, he will settle it for her. And tell her that it will all be done very discreetly.'

The page went back to the maid and passed on his master's message. Incensed, she rounded on him and gave him a piece of her mind. She spoke so vigorously that Tabubu turned to the boy, saying: 'Stop arguing with that foolish girl. Come and tell me what it is all about.' So he ran to Tabubu and delivered the same message to her, again saying that whatever they did would be managed with the greatest discretion. 'Go to Khaemwese,' answered Tabubu, 'and tell him that I am a lady of priestly rank and no ordinary being. And add that if he wishes to do anything with me, he must come down to Bubastis and visit me in my own house. There he will find everything ready, and he may do whatever he wants without any risk of anyone discovering what goes on.

When the page returned to his master and delivered Tabubu's message, Khaemwese said, 'That sounds splendid.' But everyone in his company was quite shocked.

Khaemwese was so struck by the beauty of Tabubu and so intrigued by her unusual behavior that he forgot his position and his responsibilities. He determined to accept her invitation and ordered his traveling boat to be made ready. As soon as possible he went on board and traveled downstream to Bubastis. At the west end of the town he found a tall house set in a broad enclosure with a fine garden to the north and a terrace laid out in front of the door. When he enquired he was told that it was indeed Tabubu's house, and he went into the garden to wait while his arrival was announced. Shortly afterward Tabubu came down, and taking Khaemwese by the hand, greeted him warmly: 'By the prosperity of the house of the priest of Bastet of Ankhtawy to which you have come, it would delight me greatly if you would come in with me.'

Together they went upstairs, and there Khaemwese found a

Gilded bed with sides in the form of the hippopotamus goddess
Thoeris from Tutankhamon's tomb. Cairo Museum.

splendid room. It was spotlessly clean, its ceiling was inlaid
with lapis-lazuli and turquoise, and it was furnished with five
couches spread with the best cloths; the dining table was laid
with gold plate. Wine was poured into a gold cup, and Tabubu
invited him to eat. 'I am not hungry,' Khaemwese confessed.
So incense was burnt and fine oils brought for anointing, and
the two spent a very gay day together. Khaemwese had never
come across such a woman as Tabubu. But when at last he
said, 'Let us now do what we have come here to do,' she
answered: 'You will go back to your own house. I am a lady of
priestly rank and no ordinary being. If you want to have your
way with me, first draw up a deed of maintenance on my behalf,
and also one concerning all your property. 'Fetch the local
schoolmaster,' said Khaemwese. And when he had come, he
acted as scribe and drew up the necessary legal documents
that secured for Tabubu what she wanted.

At that moment a servant announced that Khaemwese's
children were below, and he ordered them to be brought up.

Meanwhile Tabubu had put on a robe of such fine linen that her whole body was visible through it. When Khaemwese saw her, his desire was even greater and he said, 'Come now, let me do what I came here to do.' But again Tabubu reminded him of her rank and condition: 'If you want to accomplish your desire, get your children to add their signatures to these documents so that in the future there will be no argument between them and my children.' So Khaemwese called in his children and made them witness the documents.

There was, however, no satisfying the demands of Tabubu, and when Khaemwese again asked her to fulfill her promise, she once more repeated her previous reservations: 'You will go back to your own house. I am a lady of priestly rank and no ordinary being. If you want to do what you wish with me, first have the children killed, for I do not want them left to fight with my children over your property.' In desperation Khaemwese said, 'Let this terrible thing which you find so necessary be done.' So she had them killed in front of him, and their bodies were thrown out of the window to the dogs and cats below. As Khaemwese sat drinking with Tabubu, he could

hear the animals tearing at his children's flesh outside.

Nevertheless the desire remained, and he repeated his request to satisfy his wish: 'After all,' he said, 'I have done everything you have asked.' So she took him into another room in which there stood a bed made of ivory and ebony, and they lay down together. At last he seemed to be on the point of achieving what he wanted, but as he stretched out his hand to touch Tabubu she let out a great cry. In that moment he seemed to wake up, as from a dream, and he found himself lying there with no clothes on, sweating heavily and in a state of considerable excitement. Just then he saw a chariot passing by attended by many runners, and the man in it looked like Pharaoh. Khaemwese felt he ought to jump up in respect, but could not bring himself to do so in the condition he was in.

The Pharaoh saw him, and called out, 'Why, Khaemwese, are you in this state?' 'It is Neferkaptah who has done it all to me,' answered his son. 'Go now to Memphis,' said Ramesses, 'and you will find your children there standing before the king.' To this Khaemwese replied, 'My good lord, how can I go with no clothes on?' So Pharaoh ordered one of his attendants to give Khaemwese clothes.

When he was ready, Khaemwese set out for Memphis, and there he found his children alive and well. He embraced them warmly, and Pharaoh said to him: 'Were you drunk when I last saw you?' Khaemwese told him the whole story of himself and Tabubu and how Neferkaptah was involved also.

The Pharaoh did not seem to be very surprised. 'I did what I could to advise you before. If you do not take that magical book back to its place, they will certainly kill you. Take the book back, protecting yourself with a forked stick in your hand and a lighted brazier on your head.'

Khaemwese, realizing that he had acted very foolishly, humbly accepted the advice of his royal father. He took a forked stick in his hand, put a lighted brazier on his head and set out from the royal palace to return the magical book. He descended once more into the tomb, feeling far less confident than on his first visit. As soon as Ahwere saw him she called out, 'You owe it to the great god Ptah that you have returned safely, O High Priest!' Neferkaptah, however, laughed out loud at Khaemwese's humble approach. 'It's your own fault,' he cried. 'I told you what would happen.' Khaemwese greeted them both warmly and laid the book down between them. And the tomb was once more flooded with light.

BOOKS TO READ

There are numerous books on the ancient Egyptians — their history, art, archeology, religion, etc. — and any sound one must pay considerable attention to their literature. It is somewhat more difficult to find English translations of the myths, legends, and other stories. We list the most accessible ones — 'accessible' because of their price, their recent printings, and their attempt to communicate with the general public.

The Literature of the Egyptians. E. A. Wallis Budge. (In preparation).
The Ancient Egyptians: a sourcebook of their writings. Adolf Erman (trans. Blackman). Harper, 1966.
Egypt of the Pharaohs. Alan Gardiner. Oxford, 1961.
Wings of the Falcon. Joseph Kaster (ed.). Holt, 1968.
The Land of the Enchanters. B. Lewis (ed.). Harvill, 1948.
Popular Stories of Ancient Egypt. G. Maspero. (trans. Johns). Dover, 1970.
Egyptian Tales. W. M. Flinders Petrie. (2 vols.). Methuen, 1899.

MUSEUMS TO VISIT

Nothing makes the literature of the Egyptians seem quite so real as to see some of the actual preserved works, such as papyri or inscribed statues. In the introduction to each story, we have indicated where its source might be viewed today. But quite aside from the writings, collections of Egyptian antiquities offer many insights into the thoughts and activities that gave rise to the writings. In the United States, the finest collection is in The Metropolitan Museum of Art in New York City; closely following this in importance are the collections in The Brooklyn Museum of New York City and The Museum of Fine Arts in Boston. Canadians have an important collection in the Royal Ontario Museum in Toronto. We offer below a list of the other collections in the United States — all open, within certain restrictions, to the general public.

Arkansas: Little Rock Museum of Science & Natural History. *California:* Berkeley: Pacific School of Religion, Palestine Institute Museum; University of California, Robert H. Lowie Museum of Anthropology. *Georgia:* Atlanta: Emory University Museum. *Illinois:* Chicago: Natural History Museum; University of Chicago, Oriental Institute Museum; Urbana: University of Illinois, Classical & European Culture Museum. *Kentucky:* The Louisville Museum. *Maryland:* Baltimore: The Walters Art Gallery. *Massachusetts:* Cambridge: Harvard University Semitic Museum. *Michigan:* Detroit: The Detroit Institute of Arts; Wayne State University Museum of Anthropology. *Missouri:* Kansas City Museum of History and Science; The City Art Museum of St. Louis. *Ohio:* Cleveland: The Cleveland Museum of Art; The Western Reserve Historical Society; The Toledo Museum of Art. *Pennsylvania:* Philadelphia: The University Museum; Pittsburgh: Carnegie Institute Museum. *Virginia:* Richmond: The Virginia Museum of Fine Arts.

INDEX

Page numbers in boldface
refer to illustrations of
archaeological objects

OTHER TITLES IN THE SERIES

The GROSSET ALL-COLOR GUIDES provide a library of authoritative information for readers of all ages. Each comprehensive text with its specially designed illustrations yields a unique insight into a particular area of man's interests and culture.

NOW AVAILABLE

SOON TO BE PUBLISHED